THE MANAGEMENT OF
SCIENTIFIC TALENT

CONTRIBUTORS

Burton F. Barrows

Ralph E. Burgess

Theodore A. Burtis

C. A. Day

Arnold R. Deutsch

John A. Field

William P. Gage

Elisha Gray, II

Estill I. Green

John R. Hinrichs

W. M. Hoyt

Sidney L. Jones

I. Milton LeBaron

Wilbur C. Myers

E. R. Piore

Jules D. Porsche

H. J. Rand

Richard O. Roblin

Paul L. Salzberg

W. D. Seyfried

Edward A. Shaw

C. Guy Suits

Gordon K. Teal

Charles W. G. Van Horn

Jesse Werner

EDITOR

Jerome W. Blood

THE
MANAGEMENT
OF
SCIENTIFIC
TALENT

AMERICAN MANAGEMENT ASSOCIATION
NEW YORK

This is No. 76 in the series of AMA Management Reports.

FOREWORD

M OST COMPANIES DO NOT GET AS much for their research and engineering dollar as they could. In fact, the greatest waste in many firms is found in technical activities: time, money, manpower, facilities, resources, and management talent are not effectively utilized. Yet the whole future of the company—its profits, its growth, and its stability—depends upon its technical capabilities.

The reason for this state of affairs is twofold. Management has been preoccupied with the many other areas that are important to a corporation's going operations. Technical activities have assumed a position of major importance in the total management picture only relatively recently, and this has resulted in a degree of neglect. Then, too, scientists —thinking that they could achieve better results if each man were allowed to go off in a direction of his own choosing—have "lobbied" for a hands-off management attitude toward technical programs. Of course, those who shouted the loudest in the interests of freedom were often those who weren't too sure that their own work would stand up under any kind of scrutiny at all. These, then, are the two sides of the picture. Management is preoccupied with many pressing problems, while scientists and engineers, unaware of the need for closer integration into the overall corporate effort and for better coordination of their own operations, are concerned with the question of greater freedom.

If we examine the annual reports of corporation after corporation and compare the current year's sales with the sales figure reported ten years ago, we will find that in the past ten years the sales of some of these companies have increased two times, three times, six times, ten times, and as much as 25 times. When we look behind these figures, we find that for the most part this growth has been based on the utilization of new technology. If we have the opportunity of looking still deeper into the operations of these companies, we find that in every case those that have grown the most have done so because their technical programs were better managed than those of their competitors. As more firms become aware of this fact, more attention is being paid to better management of technical programs.

However, recognizing the need for well-managed technical programs doesn't solve the problem of how to find men who are qualified by training, experience, and personal interests for managerial assignments in technical-activity areas. To do a good job, research managers—all the way from project leaders to vice presidents—must be competent and experienced in scientific areas if they are to execute their managerial duties effectively. And yet this is a difficult combination of characteristics to find.

Many otherwise good candidates for these jobs, both from within and outside of the corporation, have had technical training but no real experience in the technical organization because they gained their experience in other areas of the business. These men have made poor research managers. On the other hand, many technical people have no interest in management; their interest lies in furthering their scientific capabilities. These men either aren't available for management assignments or, if forced into this role, accept the job half-heartedly and try to carry on their management responsibilities along with their scientific work. As a consequence, their performance is mediocre in both capacities.

In any case, sound management techniques must be applied to the management of research, and a balance must be maintained between the needs of the company and those of the individual researcher. It is our hope that this book will help those responsible for managing research in industry in this task.

PHILIP MARVIN
Manager, Research and Development Division

CONTENTS

INTRODUCTION

THE SCIENTIFIC REVOLUTION •

H. J. RAND

T RULY, WE ARE LIVING in an amazing age. Progress today is no longer moving along an even, upward curve but, instead, is exploding in logarithmic fashion. For this reason, the best way to gain a useful notion of the shape of things to come is first to look backward and estimate the rate of progress since 1900, then to project this rate into the future to achieve some reasonable estimate of what we may expect in the year 2000. I am, of course, well aware that there are many barriers in the way of progress that cannot be taken into consideration in such a broad discussion as this. For this reason, I shall attempt to be conservative in my projections, giving minimum rather than maximum expectations.

It is difficult to discern change, whatever its dimensions, when it is taking place very close to us, but in the years approaching A.D. 2000 a tremendous revolution will take place. The revolutionists of the future will be the scientists and engineers. This key group will work radical changes in our lives, turning old "impossibles" into "possibles" and breaking through to new frontiers in medicine, production, transportation, and nearly all phases of our economic lives. This group must keep alert, openminded, and ever aware of new methods and materials. The record of the past proves that our future lies with the men of science. They will work wonders that no magician would dare contemplate, weaving tapestries of metal, making houses of fiber and plastic, creating new cloths, new metals, new foods, new plants.

THE FUTURE OF TRANSPORTATION

To begin with, since what is in the air is much in our minds these days, let us consider aircraft. The speed of the airplane in the past 50 years picked up rather slowly, reaching a little more than 100 mph in 1918, doubling within the next decade, then reaching the amazing rates of 300 mph in 1936 and 600 mph in 1954. The present speed record

H. J. RAND is President, Rand Development Corporation, Cleveland, Ohio.

is over 2,000 mph, but we now know that rockets go around the world in remarkably short time.

In its early days, the aircraft was virtually all wing; in recent years, however, the wings have shrunk and shrunk, until in today's X-2 and X-3 rocket aircraft they are mere vestigial stubs. We can expect them to disappear altogether in the very near future.

As for materials, the aircraft manufacturer started out with wood and fabric, then gradually took advantage of the newly discovered "miracle" metal, aluminum. We are now in the era of titanium, which is only in its infancy; yet we are already graduating to high-temperature steels, with the strong possibility of entering soon the age of high-temperature plastics with low heat conductivity. In our flights into space, the occasions of exit from and re-entry into the earth's atmosphere impose a severe strain upon the structure of the aircraft. These occasions last only seconds or minutes, however, and, although plastics char, their low heat conductivity permits only the outer layers to be destroyed, leaving the structure of the space ships intact.

Our future forms of transportation are difficult to predict. Since 1900, when all transportation was either drawn by horse or powered by steam, we have witnessed the development of a number of new means of transportation, including the automobile, the truck, and the airplane. One result of this diversification and expansion of our transportation facilities has been the creation of an enormous problem in traffic control. It is my belief that most of the long-range transportation of goods and materials in the year 2000 will be carried on by unmanned space vehicles automatically and safely controlled from origin to destination along predetermined "spaceways."

If by the year 2000 we have learned to control nuclear reactions sufficiently, we will be able to send photonic rocket ships into outer space at speeds approximating that of light. This would put us in a position to examine some of the paradoxes of Einstein's equations, which indicate that as man goes into space, approaching the speed of light, he gets smaller and smaller and heavier and heavier, and his life process grows increasingly slow. Thus, theoretically at least, a man might travel into outer space for what seems to him a day, only to find on his return that 1,000 years of life had elapsed on earth.

FUELS AND ENERGY

Whatever the exact nature of our transportation in the year 2000, one thing is certain: our means of powering this transportation will be different from the fuels in common use today.

Looking backward, we find that half of all the oil consumed in the history of mankind was consumed in the past 25 years. One of our current superbombers consumes more fuel in a single mission than most of our Air Force used in 1918; and our Strategic Air Command can drop in one raid more explosive power than was expended in all of World War II, both on the ground and in the air, by all armed forces.

By the year 2000 we should be very much aware of the limited amounts of cheap fossil fuels (oil, coal, and natural gas) available. Hydroelectric power will have been utilized to the maximum. Atomic energy will be commonplace. It is hoped that the problems of atomic fusion will by then have been solved, enabling us to control the hydrogen bomb reaction. It is believed by many that controlled atomic fusion at the present time is approximately in the same stage of development as atomic fission was in 1940. The theory has been worked; what remains is the practical application. We must learn how to control temperatures of approximately 100 million degrees and to contain such temperatures.

A discussion of this matter with German scientists, who have as yet no need for secrecy, reveals that they believe the problem is solvable by means of electromagnetic fields which will hold the hydrogen-reacting atoms in the center of a large pipe, so that a few feet of space and radiant shields could contain the fantastic heat generated. The necessary isotopes for this reaction might be obtained from the sea. It is thought by some that a cubic mile of sea water contains enough of these isotopes to supply the annual energy requirements of the world in the year 2000. If this is true, and we are able to tap this source, it will change our whole way of life. We will be mining the sea instead of the land; and since we will have to process this enormous amount of water (one cubic mile) in order to derive our energy, it will no doubt be economically feasible to extract gold, silver, iodine, bromine, tungsten, and all of the sea's other rich contents as well—just as we now extract magnesium. At the same time, we will probably be farming the sea, too, growing foods not even dreamed of at the present time, most of which probably will be unicellular animals and plants. This would make available adequate food for our expanding population for at least the next century.

METALS, PLASTICS, AND SYNTHETICS

It is clear that a revolution in metals is just starting and that the next 40 years will see startling refinements in steel, aluminum, copper, and other basic metals, as well as the birth of a host of new metals and alloys. Even now a process exists for giving ordinary cast iron the properties of stainless steel. These new metals will open new frontiers and destroy old barriers to accomplishment—particularly in the fields of transportation (where they will be used to produce ships and trains of undreamed-of prowess) and production (where they will result in a myriad of new techniques and products).

In the past 50 years there has been tremendous progress in the field of plastics, primarily in the development of cast or molded forms. Yet this field is still in its infancy, with untold wonders lying ahead—plastics that will be nearly as strong as steel or which, combined with fibers, will support whole bridges. In the Rand Laboratories, for example, we have already developed a fiber-and-plastic combination which greatly improves the plastic construction presently used in boats. There is no doubt that new and better plastics will be forthcoming, including some which will withstand temperatures of many thousands of degrees.

We are witnessing today the development of engineered plastics in which the desirable properties of several materials are combined. Reinforced fiber glass is a good example of this. The tremendous tensile strength of glass fibers is utilized through combination with polyesters or other resins which protect the fragile fibers against abrasion. Another example is the resin bonding of refractory materials such as zirconium for use in rocket nozzles. Similarly, we can expect the development of engineered alloys utilizing such metals as molybdenum. Molybdenum is one of the most efficient heat-resistant metals known, but it turns to smoke in the presence of oxygen. Already experiments are under way in which molybdenum wire is pressed into shapes and infiltrated with oxidation-resistant, relatively weak materials such as Inconel.

We may look forward to the industrial utilization of organic fibers other than glass in heat-resistant fields. By the year 2000, if not hampered too much by secrecy or lack of funds, we may expect to see a whole new family of materials not presently known to man or existing in nature. These will be created by processes similar to those which General Electric has already developed to produce the first of such materials, synthetic diamonds. The tremendous heat and pressure utilized in this process change the entire crystal structure of boron nitride into a state unknown in nature. The immediate result is that this crystal structure becomes as hard as a diamond, but it has a tremendous advantage over the diamond in that it can stand about twice the temperature. This is, of course, highly significant in grinding and polishing operations.

AGRICULTURE IN 2000 A.D.

We hear a great deal about automation these days. Who would ever think that farmers lead in this important development? Probably the last place most of us would expect to find modern techniques is "down on the farm"—but the advances in agricultural technology are truly startling.

In 1900, farming was carried on principally with animal and human musclepower, and much of our population was so engaged. Then the tractor came into use, with the result that horses have practically disappeared from the American farm scene. Today, one man accomplishes what five did in 1900. Within the past 15 years the price of mules in Tennessee and Mississippi dropped from $300 to $30—at which price it no longer pays to raise them. The so-called poor farmer in that area *must* have machines—or else he must look for work in the city.

In the past generation alone there has been greater advance in the development of farm machinery than there was in the entire previous history of mankind. Clearly, automation is already a reality in farm management—from the milking machine (a rather impressive step in itself) to the modern chicken farm, with its conveyer belts, artificial sunlight control, and automatic feeding. In such a plant, the chickens never come out of their cages until they are ready to be killed; food goes in one end, and eggs come out the other; even the droppings are automatically collected and sold as fertilizer.

The benefits of these developments in agricultural technology will be further increased by the work already done in improving our plants, animals, and poultry through selective breeding. In 1956 the semen of one bull with superior characteristics was used to inseminate 100,000 cows. And ways have been found to preserve animal semen by quick-freezing—so that it is not at all unlikely that, in A.D. 2000, cows will be giving birth to offspring whose fathers died some 40 or 50 years before.

As the population grows and the demand for food increases, we can expect to see electronic computers with photoelectric sensing devices and magnetic-tape programing used to control the operations of plowing, cultivating, sowing, and reaping. Thus, a farmer might sit at the console of a TV receiver and keep track of machines in a half-dozen different fields, untended by humans except for supervisory monitoring.

ELECTRONICS AND INSTRUMENTATION

The use of electronic brains to control complex operations or perform vast computations will surely be one of the most significant and dramatic aspects of the future. We have already described how such devices will be used on the farm. Without a doubt, we can also expect to see them used increasingly in factories and processing plants, in government operations at every level, in colleges and universities—and, eventually, even in the home.

In a sense, the electronic computer is the key to the future, for it will permit us to solve mathematical, engineering, and scientific problems hitherto beyond our grasp, and to build machines that will outperform any yet invented.

Giant strides have already been taken in running complex production machines by electronic instrumentation and controls. We can now machine difficult parts to tolerances closer than has ever before been possible, and we can repeat the operation indefinitely, putting the machine's instructions on magnetic tape by means of an electronic computer which "translates" them directly from blueprints. The resulting code is fed to a control mechanism which automatically guides a lathe, milling machine, or other machine tool more accurately than the most skilled machinist's hand—and takes into account the wear of the tools and the temperature of the metal with far more success than can be done by humans alone.

Looking backward to 1900, we see an enormous and rapid rise in our investment in tools to increase the productivity of the worker. The figure we have already reached—$300,000 per worker in an oil refinery—will probably have increased several fold by the year 2000. Certainly, we can expect that our investment per worker in automatic tools will increase at an astronomical rate.

THE WORLD OF CHEMISTRY

We are all aware of the great strides that have been made in chemistry in the years since 1900. We now have great plants taking nitrogen out of the air, and others producing chemical compounds and formulations which seem sheer magic. Our ability to create new materials like nylon is already impressive. Chemistry leads the parade to tomorrow, and the advances we may expect in the next 40 years will make the last look like child's play. The sea will be turned into hundreds of valuable chemicals, as the air now is. New fibers, new finishes, new materials of all kinds will come from the laboratories, affecting everything we eat, wear, or use.

Already, in the United States, refuse waters from paper production are being utilized for human consumption. We are able by the use of heat and acid to convert cellulose into a digestible sugar for conversion by yeast into protein, thus making the waste water of paper production and sawdust convertible into a sugar, which in turn is the basis for yeast growth and produces protein- and vitamin-enriched foods. Sanitation engineers will chalk up important advances of great value, both in using waste waters and in conserving our water supply. This has been a long development. In 1916 the Germans, desperate for protein, started the project in a swimming-pool-like culture bath, dumping in one ton of seed yeast to produce, overnight, 83 tons of food yeast. By the year 2000 we will be utilizing many other waste materials and sewage materials, converting them by such processes into valuable resources.

What can we do to keep abreast of this scientific wave of the future? The answer, of course, is research. But occasionally people ask, "How can we get more from our research dollar?" or "How can we best utilize the brains and abilities of our firms?" Here are nine suggestions for getting the most out of your research dollar:

1. Never stop asking questions. How can we do it better, faster, cheaper and make it more useful, more attractive, less costly?

2. Look for opportunities in those areas where technological progress is moving fastest and where major companies are willing to supply free counsel and technical advice: in metallurgy, plastics, chemicals, and automation, for example. Don't wait for these companies to come to you; seek them out.

3. Set up R&D programs of your own, even if you have little or no staff to carry them out. Such programs will define objectives and can frequently be implemented inexpensively by outside consultants.

4. Constantly look beyond your own market for opportunities where your production and sales talents can be utilized. Don't wear blinders. Fresh approaches solve old problems.

5. Try to avoid paying for work that has already been done—or "researching the research." It is often faster and less costly to derive a solution for your problem from present knowledge than to attempt to be original.

6. Specialize in narrow fields. Few can afford to carry on broad research projects covering many fields.

7. Remember that what couldn't be done is being done. Every day new discoveries are made which may make yesterday's "impossible" possible. So research risks are worth taking.

8. Always evaluate possible projects in terms of degree of feasibility; then place your research dollars on the project most likely to succeed. But persevere; many projects are stopped just short of success.

9. Be alert and quick to move in new directions when opportunity beckons. Don't set your course rigidly and steer for oblivion. Be flexible.

Our future is certainly an exciting and challenging one. The courageous who will look and plan ahead will prosper. Research is the insurance policy of this technological revolution. Management should take out ample "research insurance" against surprise—for even companies that have progressed through many capable generations may find themselves suddenly rendered obsolete by the dramatic and swift changes certain to come.

THE ROLE OF RESEARCH IN INDUSTRY •

ELISHA GRAY, II

IT HAS BECOME VERY FASHIONABLE for a company to be doing something for the space effort today. In the not-too-distant future, this magnificent technical and scientific achievement will come more closely into focus for American industry and take its rightful place in a system designed primarily for profit. One needs to look back only two decades to review the fads of American management that have swung into popularity like a pendulum—technocracy, scientific management, operations research, aptitude testing, computers, automation, atomic energy, and research itself. All held the spotlight for a time and were overplayed by their exponents; and those that endured are now in proper perspective. This phenomenon is a characteristic of Americans. A new concept comes forward, we all get on the bandwagon, and generally the pendulum overswings. Only critical self-analysis will change this, and we will have to institute the change if there is to be one.

Since World War II, attention has been focused on research, and for a time it was considered the panacea for business ills. Unless a company had a large research staff, the financial analysts did not have faith in it. If the stockholders needed a little appreciation in the market, it could be accomplished through research. For 15 years it was the be-all and end-all of American industry; no self-respecting company could amount to much without a research function.

As a result, everyone had a research group, and the philosophy of operation was to create an atmosphere not unlike a college campus—to let the great minds roam. The environment had to be conducive to great forward strides. Direction and control of research was frowned upon because it would prevent reaping the full benefits. For budgeting it was only necessary to hire some clerks. Results? Generally they were not forthcoming. In those companies where research was related to the

ELISHA GRAY, II, is Chairman of the Board, Whirlpool Corporation, Benton Harbor, Michigan.

long-range objectives of the company, research paid off. Where research was merely the fashion of the hour, management has moved in and research is no more.

We Americans have a tendency to remember the spectacular failures and overlook the steady successes. If we are to be objective in our analysis of the role of research, then we need only to look at the contribution of research in the growth and development of the United States and world economy. The contribution of research in one area, the creation of new products, is measured in many annual reports with statements such as "*X* per cent of the 1962 sales dollars came from products not on the market ten years ago." More specifically, the role played by research in a particular industry or an individual company must be tailored to the technical, social, and economic characteristics of that industry or company. The role is intensified by the basic requirement that each company is in business to make money and to generate a profit for its stockholders. Sometimes we tend to overcomplicate what we start out to accomplish. The management role is really pretty simple: managers have a dual responsibility to maintain current business in a healthy, competitive, and profitable posture and to look for new opportunities that will provide for growth and take up the slack inevitably generated by product obsolescence.

Product research must serve the current product business and create the future product businesses. Much has been written on how to manage R&D, determine the percentage of the budget to sales, and create environments. We have all seen charts comparing GNP to research spending and so forth. This we are familiar with. American management has a job to do, and that is to attain the maximum return on investment in research.

Any strategic plan is only as good as the chief executive's commitment to the plan. What are our objectives? What role do we want research to play in our current business? Do we want new products and expansion? We must remember that the researcher without direction in the form of objectives has an unlimited hunting license. If we have unlimited dollars to pour into research, perhaps our objective should be to explore the universe; but if we are in a highly competitive business, we had better limit the objectives to the current system of endeavor plus a predetermined amount of latitude.

We at Whirlpool are in the business of engineering, manufacturing, and distributing household appliances. We expect to, and actually do, operate at a profit for the benefit of our stockholders. Our objectives revolve around our desire to produce appliances to satisfy the needs and desires of people and around the necessity to make a profit for our stockholders. Our appliances are tools for living: they wash and dry the clothes we wear; they store, preserve, and prepare the food we eat; they cool, heat, and process air to provide the environment in which we live; they clean our homes and our food utensils and dishes; and they dispose of the waste material. They are components of a life-support system. So our research objectives are to provide life-support systems: fabric maintenance, food preservation, food storage, food preparation, home maintenance, environmental control, the handling of waste, and the package that encompasses the system.

To the researcher, this is direction. Does he like it? Although there is much disagreement on this point, generally he likes direction. Latitude is also provided in that, should the researcher stray beyond the limits, he has the assurance that his idea will be considered. His effort in behalf of a current product will be to push back the parameters of knowledge surrounding that product and its associated processes. There are those who deplore the association of a product with research; but in my terms of reference, research is progressive inquiry. You can get as basic as you want so long as you do not lose sight of the concept that return on investment also applies to research.

Therefore, the research department must provide technical insurance to the current product line by extending knowledge and furnishing scientific intelligence. The knowledge gathered and developed must be applied to the current product, and feasibility must be established. If this technical progression has deviated to the extent that some new concepts are emerging, we had better parallel the technical development with marketing strategy so that when the point of an economic decision is reached, we will have developed a product and a way to sell it. This responsibility of research will give us, first, product improvement—the restoring of newness and resulting customer enthusiasm, which will aid in maintaining volume and selling price. Second, by process improvement, profit margins can be maintained, even in the face of declining selling prices, by lowering the product cost.

If this were the total role of research, the technical and scientific contribution would probably keep us tied to or, hopefully, a little ahead of our competition. At best, however, this aging process requires that a company have a reasonably balanced portfolio of products of various ages just to maintain steady profits. To sustain corporate growth and earnings, it becomes necessary to introduce new products that serve emerging needs of people and add income with higher profit margins.

Research must produce the new products to sustain corporate growth. Some will come as the result of research within the company. Other new products will come as the result of research outside the company, and we can only hope that our scientific and technical staff will be ready to accept them. Some will come from research planning, which should be an integral part of corporate research activity. The planners should be constantly alert to new opportunities that result from change—technical, marketing, social, or economic. Constant re-evaluation of plans, progress, and opportunities by the planners will result in more specific direction. So far, only product research has been discussed, but as much emphasis is needed on marketing. Great technical strides have been made in the past 20 years, but we market our goods much the same now as we did two decades ago. Some challenges have been made to the system of distribution, but the resultant changes have been gradual.

Thus, what is the role of research in industry? First of all, research must continue to push back the parameters of knowledge of our current product lines and to maintain the lines of intelligence from a technical and scientific standpoint. Second, it must be the focal point for the creation of new products and new profit opportunities. The responsibility of research must go beyond the classical technical role to include research planning and the establishing of marketing plans.

Research has opened up a limitless frontier for American business, but daring will be required to explore these new frontiers. The rewards will be rich for imaginative, flexible, and technically skilled companies. Technical competence alone will not do the job; it must be matched by the marketing, social, and economic components of the system.

THE MANAGEABILITY OF
SCIENTIFIC RESEARCH •

C. GUY SUITS

SCIENCE AND MANAGING BEGAN to associate with each other approximately 50 years ago. At first the association was only tenuous. Some pioneers in the profession of managing decided in 1910 that a convenient name for the new philosophy they were developing would be "scientific management." At about the same time scientific research was beginning to be performed on an organized basis. Although scientists, by their nature and tradition, tended to resist the idea of managing or being managed, the fact remains that the "management of science" became as inevitable as "scientific management."

Relations between these two disciplines—or, if you prefer, professions— have not always been as close as the names might indicate. Scientists have been skeptical about how much science is actually involved in "scientific management," and managers have openly doubted that scientific research *can* be managed. Many scientists have been less than enthusiastic over the idea that "the scientific method"—involving, particularly, the reproducible experiment—*can* be applied to a subject like management. On the other side, it has been said that "a good professional manager can manage anything"—"except research," one usually adds. There has been some agreement, particularly on the part of the scientist, that in research, good management, like good government, is that which manages the least.

But in spite of some prejudices arising from professional prerogatives, science and managing are becoming mutually indispensable. I think most scientists would agree that modern management, with its intensive analysis of its functions, and with its computers and cybernetics, is becoming

C. GUY SUITS is Vice President and Director of Research, General Electric Company, Schenectady, New York.

more "scientific." We can conclude that any multibillion-dollar business such as research is today will have to develop some business management, even at the cost of some professional discomfort on the part of both managers and researchers. Research is, of course, not a "business" in the ordinary sense—it is usually a functional part of many businesses. There is no doubt, however, that the aggregate expenditure for this work is in the billion-dollar range and growing rapidly. Thus, the argument of this chapter is that management and research must get together to study mutually important problems. If we can make some progress here—and I am sure that we can—it will expand the usefulness of this highly creative work in industry and will provide increasing opportunities for the engineering of tomorrow's products, processes, and services.

"Research" is a broad term that includes a great variety of technical work, and I now wish to focus more closely on industrial scientific research including hopefully some basic research. It is in this variety of research that the greatest challenges and opportunities for management lie. I think it is timely to discuss the management aspects of scientific research, because a great many people in industry and in government are re-examining their interest in this kind of work.

I have observed frequently that businessmen who feel entirely comfortable about the management aspects of engineering, manufacturing, and marketing may feel baffled when it comes to scientific research. Much of this discomfort arises from the difficulty of putting numbers on the quantities with which we deal in the management of research. This is a serious difficulty, and I feel that we will not develop the full potential of this industrial activity until we acquire more facility in measurement. The only thing about research that we measure very well at present is the expense input. That particular index we measure with great competence.

In spite of some management difficulties—and to make a point I have exaggerated a bit—research (including basic research) is rapidly growing in American industry. The statistics, which are probably familiar to the reader, are very impressive. It *must* be that research expenditures turn out well in a significant number of cases if businessmen are allocating increasing sums for this work. I can think of many instances in which it has been a good thing in our company.

Actually, scientific research may be thought of as the starting expense of an investment in technological innovation. Whether it is a good investment depends upon a lot of things, including the kind of industry in which the business is conducted. Some businesses and even whole industries seem to require very little technological innovation. In some cases that come to mind innovation is achieved annually by the rearrangement of chrome strips; this is a very powerful factor in the marketplace, because people are very reluctant to be seen with their chrome strips in the wrong place.

The other extreme is presented by the technical industries, including the fields of electrical products, electronics, chemicals, instruments, communications, semiconductors, pharmaceuticals, aviation, the defense industries, and many others. The customers for these products are generally not so impressed by chrome strips or whether the handle is right side up or upside down. It is here that technological innovation has the greatest leverage, and scientific research its greatest opportunity.

PLANNING BASIC RESEARCH

It is a too commonly accepted fact that you can't plan basic research—that is, you can't plan on what will come from the research with any certainty. It is also too obvious that if you are exploring in a strange land you can't predict what you are going to discover. Both of these things are too true and too obvious, and they are also not quite correct. A little thought will show that although a prediction of specifically what is going to be discovered, and precisely when, may be highly speculative—or even impossible—a good deal *can* be said in advance about expected discoveries. In fact, it is important in business planning to look foward as far as possible, and to do so effectively one must speculate about scientific progress. One should, to the extent possible, anticipate its probable outlines and timing, and its probable impact on industrial technology. Important in the present context is the fact that a great deal can be done by research management to plan the organization and the operation of its scientific research programs to attain the research objectives which *would* have the desired impact on important technology. To illustrate the approach, consider this question: how many metallurgists have you heard of who, in the course of their research, discovered a new antibiotic drug? Or, how many solid-state physicists do you recall who have discovered a new polymer synthesis? This leads to Rule 1: *the results of research will be heavily weighted in favor of the field of specialization of the investigator.*

Now let's take a closer look at the work of the research specialist in relation to the objective of the research. In the course of his work, the researcher is presented daily with many alternative choices and directions. He can go to a higher pressure, a lower temperature, a more dilute solution, a narrower band pass, a higher Q, a lower frequency, and so forth ad infinitum. If his research objective is clear and he is determined to reach it, he frequently can and does make the choice that favors his objective. Because this is so, we regard the attainment of the objective as a very probable result of his investigation.

Successful researchers, whether in industry or elsewhere, do not plod through their scientific careers stumbling upon things accidentally—that is, they don't constantly stumble upon *important* things. Some strikingly successful research careers, like that of Irving Langmuir, have been characterized by a constant succession of important research results. Powerful innate curiosity and many other unusual aptitudes are involved in such cases, but one cannot avoid the conclusion that some careful sorting out of trivia, and the selection of important objectives, has played a decisive role in such careers. I conclude that a knowledge of what to look for and of what would be important if it could be found is a source of motivation and guidance that significantly influences the results of research. This leads to Rule 2: *motivation is a very important management practice in planning and operating research programs.*

ORGANIZATION OF TECHNICAL WORK

Organization, as an element of management, has been experiencing growth and evolution as our economy has been growing, and this evolution has extended to the organizational components for doing technical work. The location of these components—for example, laboratories—in a decentralized company is a problem which I once thought was confined to a few large companies. This seems not to be the case, for there is a lively interest in the subject in companies large and small. A decentralized operating plan may be an operating necessity for a large company for reasons of size, but it may be equally necessary or desirable in small and medium-size companies because of product or market diversity or geographical dispersion.

In all of these cases, the matter of organizational location of laboratories is involved, and from the variety of different plans being tried by different companies it appears that no single "best" solution is in prospect. Again, companies differ, and each individual solution must be designed to meet all of the environmental circumstances of the particular industry and company involved. Specifically, one of the significant circumstances that must be taken into account in the planning of organizations is the nature of the technical work itself. The character of the work, for example, may be such that the choice between one central laboratory and five decentralized laboratories may not be a free choice at all. Or it may be that the cost of doing the work will be substantially different in the two cases. That this should be so in the case of research work is not too surprising, because similar considerations apply to other industrial operations. For example, the large manufacturing plant required for the production of steam turbines might produce very uneconomically, or not at all, if divided into five small plants geographically dispersed. Some scientific and technical operations have a "critical size" imposed by the requirement of a great variety of technical skills or facilities. Fragmentation may reduce the effectiveness of such units almost to zero. Complex and expensive gear and equipment so characterize much modern scientific research that the economy, utilization, and duplication of research investment must be taken into account explicitly in considering organizational alternatives.

In the company with which I am associated, where we regard a decentralized plan as an operating necessity, we have been able to sort out these interrelated problems of organization and technical work successfully. Our *product-oriented* laboratories are located in the decentralized operating or business components of the company. Our *science-oriented* laboratory is a "service" component serving the operating components and the company as a whole; its objective is not products, but *opportunities for new technology,* embodied in ideas, phenomena, materials, and processes that originate in scientific research. Whether the "opportunity" is translated into a product or a business is a decentralized decision, in which Research Services has a great interest but no authority.

OPERATING CONSIDERATIONS IN SCIENTIFIC RESEARCH

Because there is in industry far more experience in the management of engineering, manufacturing, and marketing, we frequently employ practices in managing research that are more suited to these older fields. For example, it is appropriate in an engineering development activity that is geared to a product plan to require weekly or monthly reports of progress. In an overall business plan, these reports are very valuable because they make possible the coordination of the various functions involved and permit a measure of progress in comparison to the plan. In a scientific research program, we have found that the requirement of reports on a calendar basis is unrealistic. The results of scientific research investigations do not emerge with chronological regularity. There may be no result for five months, and a jackpot a day later. Any ingenious researcher can produce a one-inch-thick report each week, if required. But he may have time for little else, and most of his reports will be extremely dull reading. A better plan, we feel, is to require that reports be written only when there is something to report, regardless of the calendar. The reports that are written on this plan are worth reading. Furthermore, the scientist who issues reports opportunely is on your team, because he knows that you understand the nature of the work in which he is engaged and have conformed your management procedure to this understanding.

Communication is a very important activity in industrial scientific research, and some intensive attention to the subject is required to attain satisfaction at all points in an industrial organization. Let us consider first the problem of internal communication associated with technical work programs. We must keep in mind that the transition of an idea from scientific research to the point of utilization by an ultimate consumer may require many steps in technological, engineering, and manufacturing development. The applied scientist, the development engineer, the designer, the test engineer, the manufacturing engineer, and a host of other specialists may each contribute essential elements to the successful transition. Communication from one step to the next is a minimum requirement in a transition of this kind, and the steps must not be so large that people have difficulty in communicating, even by shouting. The problem of effective communication thus cannot be solved without reference to organizational concepts.

MEASUREMENTS OF SCIENTIFIC RESEARCH

In the professional work of the research scientist, *measurement* is an essential activity. A theory of nature is not truly descriptive until it becomes quantitative, nor is a scientific observation fully meaningful until numbers can be associated with the phenomena under study. This being the case, it is surprising that scientists themselves have shown little interest in measurements of their functional work. Such measurements are a necessity if scientific research is to grow in magnitude and in contribution in American industry.

The measurements required include (1) the individual achievement and productivity of the research scientist, and (2) the overall result of a research project on company operations.

Some progress is being made in identifying the elements of output of a research organization, and by the example of these methods we may one day learn how to measure the performance and productivity of the individual research scientist. That result is earnestly desired, because we wish to recognize promptly his achievement and to reward him equitably for his work. The recognition I have in mind is not recognition in the world of science—for, although such recognition is also very important to a scientist, it may take place a distressingly long time after his immediate associates, his colleagues, and his organization are aware of his ability and accomplishment.

Some elements of the output of a research organization are readily apparent; they include leadership, scientific papers, reports, patents, and consultation. Some time ago an interesting analysis of the "paper product" of numerous research groups was published, and it explored some correlations with salary levels.* More analyses of this kind and quality are much needed and could greatly extend our knowledge of scientific productivity. The direction of progress for the measurement of individual scientific productivity seems clear. We must identify all of the elements of output, weigh them, and measure them. Patents, for example, undoubtedly provide an index of output, but this index is presently of more value as a statistical measurement than as an individual measurement. Patents differ greatly in value. Furthermore, the value of a patent may depend upon time in an unpredictable manner. A patent which appeared to have limited promise when issued might at a later date acquire great value because of additional developments in related fields; or the contrary might be true. Although we don't know how to measure the value of scientific papers, it is certain that they differ greatly in their contribution to science. Indexes over and above the "paper product" are clearly required. For example, some very valuable members of a research staff publish few papers and apply for few patents. Their contribution lies in leadership which they impart through counsel, advice, and consultation. No tangible index of this output lends itself readily to the measurement of this valuable work.

Now let us consider the value *to the company* of the research output we have been discussing. The appraisal of the overall company benefits of a venture which originated in research is a useful endeavor. If such studies could be projected forward, they would have greater usefulness, but even as an appraisal of the results of a completed venture they provide valuable perspective which may be brought to bear on future decisions concerning research.

The manager of a profit-making business is constantly considering a great many alternative routes for expenditures for new or expanded sales, markets, and profits. He may, for example, build *new plant capacity* for an increased volume of presently manufactured products, or he may invest in *new machinery,* including increased mechanization and automation in present manufacturing plants. On the other hand, a greater opportunity might appear to be in the *marketing* area, where a new approach and program may pay off handsomely. Alternatively he may decide on the integration of his manufacturing by extending his operations in the direction of his basic raw materials, and so forth. Or he may invest in *research.*

In all but the last of these alternatives, it is generally possible to forecast the intended result with sufficient accuracy to permit decision making. To take a simple case, if the question concerns the purchase of improved

*Shockley, William, "On the Statistics of Individual Variations of Productivity in Research Laboratories," *Proceedings of the Institute of Radio Engineers,* March 1957.

machinery for reducing manufacturing costs for an existing line of products, it is usually a straightforward matter to calculate the return on the intended investment. The calculation of the future return on present research expenditures, on the other hand, involves more intangibles, and hence is generally much more speculative. Unless the management is far-sighted, the research proposal may lose out in competition with alternative investment opportunities. Too often, when the partisan of a research proposal says that its possibilities are "incalculable," he's probably exactly right: they can't be calculated.

We must learn more about this problem through analysis and study. I am greatly encouraged by the positive usefulness of project case studies, or "model" studies, which we have undertaken in our organization. They have clearly justified the effort involved.

*   *   *

I have endeavored to show that the extension of scientific management to the management of scientific research is an increasingly important feature of modern industry. Although research directors are constantly confronted with—and occasionally confounded by—the numerous intangibles that always thwart their effort to find simple formulas for operating procedures, it is possible to find a rationale for guidance in a specific situation. It is through progress in all phases of scientific management that today's research will have increased impact upon the growth of technology, upon the opportunities for engineering tomorrow's products and services, and hence upon the growth and vitality of the economy as a whole.

DEFINING THE ROLE AND RESPONSIBILITIES OF THE RESEARCH MANAGER •

THEODORE A. BURTIS

T HE WIDELY PUBLICIZED FIGURES on the cost of industrial research in the United States are adequate testimony to the importance of this function today. It is to the research manager and his organization, more than to any other single individual or group, that companies have come to look for the protection of the sources of present profits and the development of the sources of future profits. Simply stated, then, the job of the research manager is to maintain a flow of new and improved products and processes—the raw materials from which businesses are built. Like all simple statements, unfortunately, this leaves a great deal unsaid. It is the purpose of this brief paper to attempt to provide a more detailed definition of the role and responsibilities of the research manager in a company properly devoted to profit making.

The environment in which the research manager operates has, of course, a great deal to do with the nature of the role he plays and is worth a brief examination. Unquestionably, research today has the respect and confidence of management, with little of the unhealthy, uncritical hero worship which was once in evidence or of the equally bad "long hair," "ivory tower" attitude. Even so, all is not always perfect harmony. The controller may be uncomfortable about the allocation of large sums of money to research with cheerful acceptance of the knowledge that probably fewer than half of the projects will produce any useful results; he may also be dissatisfied with the attitude of the research and development department toward budgets—a perennially touchy subject.

THEODORE A. BURTIS is President, Houdry Process and Chemical Company, Philadelphia, Pennsylvania.

The sales department may sometimes be annoyed because the research and development department will not drop everything else to solve the immediate problem of some unhappy customer. And, finally, the manufacturing department may be perplexed at the desire of the research and development people always to rock the boat—to upset a smooth-running plant in order to try something new and unproven. The importance of these frictions can easily be exaggerated, but they do seem to exist to some degree in most organizations, and they do affect the job of the research manager.

In this environment of general confidence tempered with some elements of friction, then, what should be expected of the research manager? His job has two aspects, related and even overlapping in practice, but conveniently subject to separate examination. These are (1) the task of running the research organization and (2) the task of maintaining contact with the rest of the company and coordinating research efforts with those of other organizational elements.

RUNNING THE RESEARCH ORGANIZATION

In his line management job, the research manager must above all be a manager—that is, one who gets things done through others, rather than one who does things himself. Whether he is a scientist by training who has acquired administrative and managerial responsibilities or a specialist by training in some other discipline, he must be prepared for the most part to give up his own specialty as the focus of his daily effort. Instead, he must turn his attention to the task of building an organization, selecting and training people qualified to do the job at hand, seeing that they know what the job is, and then letting them do it—with encouragement and advice but with a minimum of interference. He must set up the machinery to handle the general administrative tasks: the provision of supplies and services, the administration of salary and wage programs, and the myriad other organizational details which are necessary. For his own part, he is personally faced with the problem of encouraging creativity and imagination in his staff and, at the same time, exercising the necessary controls to channel these forces into productive areas. It will rest largely with him to strike a balance between the defensive elements of research and development which are needed to maintain the position of his company's present products in their market and the offensive type of research aimed at creating new products or opening up entirely new fields of endeavor.

It is in this area of planning and programing that the research manager faces his greatest challenge. Assuming for the moment that the general management of his company has defined its goals, let us consider the role of the research manager within his own organization.

There has been a great deal of nonsense about the "peculiarities" of research scientists and engineers: their reputed introversion, their "mechanical" minds, their extreme individualism, their rejection of all restraint, and a dozen other false generalizations. No doubt there do exist scientists and engineers with some or all of these characteristics; and the fact that the men in our laboratories have chosen research as a career would certainly seem to indicate that they have a built-in impatience with the status quo. I think it is a far more valid generalization, however, that research scientists and engineers are intelligent people and loyal employees who want to know the boundaries within which they are expected to work.

It is the characteristic of a good research organization that the number of ideas it generates far exceeds the availability of time, money, or manpower needed for their exploitation. Since there is naturally a certain pride of authorship associated with the generation of ideas, there will always be for the research manager the problem of carefully and diplomatically selecting the ideas which are to be pursued. Assuming once more that the company management has stated its general objectives clearly, it is an important responsibility of the research manager to see that the scope and direction of the research program are equally well defined. When this has been done, and the resulting definitions have been properly communicated to the research staff, it may be expected that the ideas generated by the research staff will at least conform in general to the outline of the program which the company wishes to pursue. Inevitably, however, it will be necessary to eliminate some ideas because they do not hold promise—or more probably, because, in the judgment of research management, others are more appropriate or hold more promise for the company's future. A great deal can be accomplished in this selection through the intelligent use of technical and economic studies, and it can be expected that these tools themselves will narrow the area of selection. In the last analysis, however, project selection is largely a matter of judgment, and the research manager must be the final referee.

If the research manager has been afforded a proper delegation of responsibility and authority, he will have wide discretion in the selection of projects. This is particularly essential with regard to that stage of research which is characterized as exploratory or even speculative. In the normal course of events, the research manager may expect to have put before him quite a few proposals which can yield a modest, but almost certain, benefit to his company. He has the obligation, of course, to see that some of these are pursued. More important, however, the good research manager must have what we might call an "educated gambling instinct" and must be willing to play some promising long shots. It may be true, as is often said, that research is by its very nature a gamble. This should not be taken to mean, however, that all the skill and resources of the research and development department should be played on long shots. Caution is clearly called for—though not, of course, to the degree that only the nearly certain projects are pursued. Some long shots have paid off handsomely, usually as the result of the dedication of some individual backed up by a research manager with the courage to stay in the game when the going was rough.

The courage to back up a long shot should be balanced by another kind of courage: the courage to quit. It often seems that this kind of courage is even more difficult to come by. Since research is largely unpredictable and progress is usually made by small steps, and because research men by their very nature are eternally hopeful and optimistic, the research manager will often be faced with a plea for "just one more thousand dollars" or "just one more week's work" or "just one more *something*" which it is hoped will clear up the difficulties that seem to be bogging down progress. It takes not only good judgment but courage as well to decide to abandon a project, particularly if a considerable amount of money has been spent on it. It is quite generally accepted that somewhere between 50 and 90 per cent of all research projects come to no useful end. It obviously makes a great deal of difference, however, whether the 50 or 90 per cent was dropped after a thousand dollars had been spent or after a hundred thousand dollars had been spent.

The courage to continue when the going is rough and the courage to quit when the prospects fade—these call for a tough-mindedness on the part of the research manager without which he cannot possibly hope to be effective in his job. This is, of course, an aspect of the function of review and control; it is emphasized here, however, because it has such extreme significance for research and development.

COORDINATING RESEARCH WITH COMPANY OBJECTIVES

Up to this point it has been assumed that the company management has thought out and stated its objectives, goals, and policies and has properly communicated them to the organization, and specifically to the research department. Unfortunately, this is not always a safe assumption, and its significance should be examined.

This, of course, is where the research manager's second role comes in. Whatever else it may be, a research and development department is certainly not an "ivory tower," and it cannot function in a vacuum any more effectively than can any other department of the company. It would hardly seem necessary these days to point out that, if a research manager is to keep his company at the head of the parade, he ought to know what parade he is supposed to lead. More and more company managements today realize the need to think out and state the objectives of their business. Particularly in smaller companies, however, there is likely to remain the feeling that writing these goals down on paper is unnecessary because "we all know what we want to do." If this is true, then stating the objectives in writing should not be very difficult. If it *is* difficult, then "we" clearly do not know the goals very well and should quickly decide what they are.

Research management should have a voice in deciding what the company's objectives are and what its own particular goals should be. It will make a great deal of difference to research in its programing and prosecution, for example, whether the company intends to base its future on the exploitation of a particular raw material, chooses to follow a particular market, or has special competence in some area of technology on which to build the future of the business.

The difference in size and type of research effort stemming from such decisions as these can be seen clearly in American industry. Within the petroleum industry, for example, it is quite apparent that some companies must at some time have decided that they are primarily crude-oil producers and that refining and marketing are secondary to crude production. Such companies generally have extensive geophysical and exploration laboratories but few process laboratories for refining. Other companies have apparently decided that they are producers and marketers of fuels of all types and have not only extensive refinery facilities but substantial laboratories devoted to the development of all kinds of fuels and lubricants. Still other companies have apparently gone a step further and decided that theirs is a business based on hydrocarbons and that they will pursue this business in whatever directions technology leads them. Characteristically, these companies not only are refiners and marketers of fuel but have become major producers of petrochemicals. Perhaps these variations have developed by accident, but we would prefer to think that they are based on well-thought-out policy decisions on the part of management. The research manager has a right to expect—and even to demand—from his management a clear indication of the kind of business the company is in and the general direction it proposes to take.

Since even the best and most clearly defined goals must remain mirages if no steps are taken to reach them, plans must be made. Planning in all its ramifications has been so thoroughly analyzed in the literature of management, however, that no repetition is needed here. Suffice it to say that companywide planning is the foundation on which research programing rests. It seems scarcely controvertible that the research manager should play an indispensable and continuing role in his company's planning for the future.

The research manager has a right to expect, and must have, continuing guidance and cooperation from the other divisions in the company in setting up and carrying out the research and development program. To this end, many companies today have established a research and development committee, usually comprised of the research manager and the top officers or executives of other divisions of the company. If such a committee does not already exist in his own company, the research manager would be well advised to insist that one be established, provided that its function is clearly defined ahead of time. This is a proper review and control procedure for the company, and the use of such a committee does not imply, and should not be considered to imply, an abdication of authority or responsibility for research on the part of the research manager. If such a committee should ever reach the point where it is clearly attempting to direct the pursuit of individual research programs, it should be immediately disbanded. There is probably no group in the company less qualified to dictate detailed research programing than a committee of the top men in other divisions.

The useful purpose such a committee can serve is to provide for the research manager a review board through which he can determine whether the research program is in fact oriented to the needs of the other divisions. These other divisions of the company are ultimately the customers of the research and development department, and the manager of any well-run business is certainly aware of the need to direct his activities in such a way as to meet the needs of his customers. The committee serves the further function of providing for the research manager a means of securing the assistance and cooperation of the other departments. The research manager and his staff cannot possibly be expert in all aspects of the company's business, and it is through such a committee as this that the research manager can be assured of the availability of the services of specialists in other divisions which he will need from time to time. Unless some such organizational arrangement exists, there is a very serious danger that the research and development department may in fact become so isolated that its programs cannot be kept in harmony with the objectives of the company. The committee may also serve the very useful function of providing a meeting place in which to reconcile the conflicting demands of the various other operating divisions of the company upon research and development.

If the research manager is to carry out his job effectively within his department, there is one more thing which he has some right to expect from management, and that is stability in the company's overall research and development effort. Since research and development is by its very nature directed largely toward the future, it is particularly necessary that the company be prepared to maintain a relatively stable base for research and development, so that the research program will not be subject to sudden and violent contractions and expansions. Obviously, no organization or part of an organization can ever be completely immune to the economic pressures of business. Nevertheless, the erection of a suitable research and development structure is a long-time proposition, and the company which decides to pursue research and development should be prepared to support the organization for a reasonable period of time in spite of any short-term fluctuations in its business. When such assurance is provided, of course, the research manager must recognize his obligation to tailor the size and nature of his staff to the real needs of the job.

* * *

Given a clear definition of goals, objectives, and policies by his management; given the opportunity to participate in the long- and short-range planning of his company; given the active cooperation of other departments; and being blessed with the good judgment to select and carry out programs consistent with the company's goals, the research manager should be well able to fulfill his responsibility for providing his company with the products and processes from which its future earnings will be derived.

OBJECTIVES AND PLANNING

BASIC COMPANY POLICY REGARDING RESEARCH •

E. R. PIORE

B ASIC COMPANY POLICY REGARDING research is firmly tied to the product and business needs of the company and the customers that it serves. Research in industry is a new phenomenon. Within the lifetime of many of us, we have observed significant growth in the support of science by industry. Engineering—product development—is a much older function within our industries. The inventor and the engineer have a much longer history in the industrial world than the scientist, in terms of numbers and the resources made available to them. The industrial revolution, symbolized by the construction of factories and utilization of steam for power, was concurrent with the growth of science but not necessarily dependent upon science.

These days, technology needs the support of science, basic research, and applied research. It needs advanced development and engineering, product development, and product and manufacturing engineering, before a profitable product hits the marketplace. Invention alone cannot produce profit or economic growth in our contemporary society. Thomas A. Edison in the United States and Sir Joseph W. Swan in the United Kingdom are given credit for the invention of the carbon incandescent lamp. However, it took the best in science to make the incandescent lamp an ordinary household device. The same observation can be made regarding the phonograph and photography. Today it is difficult to invent without science. A company's scientific activities must be coupled not only to the other components of the company, as indicated above, but also to the scientific community at large. It is nurtured by this scientific community and must take an active part in it by contributing to professional societies through journals, meetings, and so forth.

E. R. PIORE is Vice President for Research and Engineering, International Business Machines Corporation, New York, New York.

The need for science in a company is the rationale for research activities. But how much and of what kind—these are questions of basic policy—to insure that the research organization fully functions appropriately to the company's needs. Basic policy is usually in the form of a mission, a set of objectives or relationships which guide the research organization's activities. There are many ways of formulating these. There is the relationship of the research organization to the rest of the company and to the scientific community on the outside. This helps formalize numerous technical and administrative organizational couplings and communications channels. It also suggests ways of evaluating the research organization. There are also objectives which contain the actual program, its goals and aspirations. These objectives determine the manner in which research resources, men, money, equipment, and space will be utilized. Generally, most companies express their research policy in terms of both objectives and relationships.

RELATIONSHIP TO THE COMPANY AND THE SCIENTIFIC COMMUNITY

A research organization must essentially operate in four ways:
1. Sustain company operations.
2. Insure the technical future.
3. Make an impact on the company.
4. Maintain an eminent position within the scientific community.
Each of these takes on specific meaning in specific companies. In IBM, for example, sustaining the company operations requires the research organization to conduct programs which relate to long-range company plans and problems. This helps to assure a sophisticated level of understanding of our present technologies, including their limits. It means also that the research organization should demonstrate the feasibility of new systems applications in order to provide IBM with new business opportunities. Insuring the technical future requires the research organization to accumulate scientific and technical knowledge with an eye toward evaluating trends and opportunities. It also means that programs must be conducted that will provide IBM development laboratories with an inventory of technologies which will allow them to pick and choose as the marketplace demands. Furthermore, this goal requires the generation of inventions and patentable ideas to maintain the company's freedom of action in areas of interest. The research organization must also make an impact on the corporation. It must participate in recruiting, training, and transfer activities in order that new technologies are made available throughout the corporation. It must seed new development projects as they are transferred to the engineering laboratories. A high level of technical com-

petence must be maintained so that the engineering laboratories have available to them an internal consulting service.

CHARACTER OF RESEARCH PROGRAMS

In looking at a research organization and large industrial organizations, three types of activity can normally be distinguished. First, there is an activity in research in which the company will attempt to be a dominating force in the scientific and engineering community. This activity is centered around the hard core of the technology pertinent to that industry. Second, there is an activity in research where the company has to be aware and understand a technology but not dominate it. It needs the technology, but the technology is not unique to that industry but common to many others. Take, for example, the science of lubrication. A computer manufacturer would probably wish to understand lubrication but need not have a large group in this area. On the other hand, he would probably be delighted to employ the best lubrication scientist in the world. Finally, there is a listening-post activity through which the company learns what is going on in the scientific community in general. The research organization wishes to understand technological trends in order to be aware of progress which may have implications in its areas of interest. An organization need not cover all areas of technology. It must be highly selective and choose only those areas which would be expected to have possible side effects.

These are the three prime areas of activity of many research organizations. Productivity will of course depend upon obtaining the right mix. Over and above these three areas, it is important that research operate in advanced technology so that its activities will be coupled with the development laboratories. There is never a sharp division between research and engineering activities, and it is therefore necessary to provide a great deal of overlap to secure technical couplings.

THE RESEARCH ENVIRONMENT

In addition to citing the objectives of the research organization, company policy must consider the research environment. Research prospers most when the scientist has freedom in selecting the problems he studies and in choosing methods for dealing with them. Most people, I think, will accept the validity of Mees's observation that in ordering ignorance we start at the top. Certainly it would appear to be generally true that in ordering ignorance of research we start at the top with the executives and work down to the knowledgeable men who do the research. Management is a service organization.

In research, as elsewhere, it is necessary to select from a broad range of possibilities the truly significant problems—and the man at the bench is best equipped to do this. The tendency to "protect" the creative mind from the realities that a company faces is one of the hidden factors that often plays havoc with a research operation.

In addition to the need for freedom to select significant problems, there is an equally important need for the researcher to be able to communicate with others so that he can be judged by his peers and receive appropriate recognition for his contributions within the scientific and engineering community in the company and outside. When internal communications barriers preclude proper evaluation and recognition of the researcher's work by the community beyond the laboratory, it becomes especially important that in-house evaluation and recognition be afforded on a professional basis. Again, this emphasizes the need for the researcher to know what business the company is engaged in and for the company to know why it supports its own research organization.

DEVELOPING RESEARCH OBJECTIVES •

C. A. DAY

T HE RAPID GROWTH IN RESEARCH activity which occurred during and after World War II has been accompanied by a corresponding increase in the literature dealing with means of organizing research, determining its objectives, and evaluating its results. A review of this literature reveals little in the way of valid techniques which can be universally applied toward the development of specific company objectives. After some reflection, I have concluded that this utopia is impossible to attain, simply because of the extreme diversity in industrial activity. Research is not a thing apart; it is woven into the warp and woof of each industry, and it follows that the extent to which it is used and the direction in which it is applied will be as different as the differences in industrial activity. If further evidence of this is necessary, one has only to note that research expenditures, expressed as a percentage of gross sales, vary between industries from a few tenths of a per cent to more than 10 per cent. Few would contend that this wide variation is a function of the intelligence of the respective managements. There is, however, one principle which can be universally applied, and this is that research objectives must be closely coordinated with the overall objectives of the company.

COORDINATING RESEARCH AND COMPANY OBJECTIVES

In establishing research objectives it is of primary importance that the research director have a clear understanding of overall company objectives, both short and long range. It is equally important that he keep abreast of any changes that occur in company objectives as a result of changes either in management or in the economic climate. It should be obvious that research-developed products or processes which are not compatible with overall company objectives have little chance of commercialization.

C. A. DAY is Manager, Chemicals Department, Richfield Oil Corporation, Los Angeles, California.

It will be particularly helpful if the company's long-range planning has reached the stage where both operating and capital budgets are prepared for a number of years into the future. Such future budgets should not, however, be regarded as inflexible; if they are, they had better not be made at all. Rather, they should be regarded as dynamic and, in this light, revised and extended for an additional year as each year passes. If used properly—that is, as rough guideposts to the future—they can be invaluable in keeping the thinking of all those concerned with management upon a solid foundation. What could be more reassuring to the research director than to know that funds have already been earmarked to capitalize on successful research that is directed toward company diversification? Here, again, I should like to warn against the fallacy of regarding such capital-budget items as inflexible. There should be no inference that budgeted capital funds will be spent even if no suitable project is available or that additional funds will not be made available if exceptionally attractive opportunities are disclosed.

In considering research objectives which represent a change in the company's basic orientation, it is important that an audit be made of those company assets and liabilities which would have a bearing on the decision. The items to be considered in such an audit are as follows:

1. *Raw materials.* If a chemical company were planning to enter the inorganic phosphate field, it could hardly afford to purchase phosphorus from a prime producer who would also be a competitor in the marketing of phosphates. On the other hand, the control of phosphorus-bearing land would be a major asset to a company entering the phosphate field. This is, of course, an obvious example, but the principle is important and should not be overlooked by companies operating in areas which are not as clearly defined.

2. *Process skills and equipment.* A strong raw materials position—in combination with special process skills and, perhaps, unusual equipment—can indicate an area in which research would be especially rewarding. The lack of a competitive supply of process skills and equipment—or at least a plan to establish them—should serve as a warning signal that research in this area might be futile.

3. *Marketing position.* A thorough evaluation of the company's ability to market a given type of product should be prerequisite to the initiation of research directed toward the ultimate production of such a product. An exceptionally strong position for marketing certain types of products may overshadow a weaker position in raw materials, process know-how, and equipment. The reverse is also true, of course, and the absence of marketing skills for a new class of products should not always outweigh exceptional advantages in other

areas. The need for establishing an adequate marketing group should, however, be recognized and considered in the overall evaluation before research in this direction is initiated.

4. *Geographic location.* Those who live and work on the West Coast are particularly conscious of the importance of geographic location. There are many products which must participate in national markets in order to provide sufficient volume for a plant of economical size. Under these conditions, a Western plant will be at a freight disadvantage. The magnitude of this liability will be in inverse proportion to the price of the product, but it will always be a liability. On the other hand, a Western location will be an asset if Western demand is equal to or approaching the output of a plant of economical size. Sometimes it will be sound business to pre-empt a growing market by building somewhat ahead of demand. This is particularly true in the West, where population is increasing at a rate faster than the country as a whole.

5. *Company size and organization.* A large organization has the advantage of being able to bring specialized skills to the various phases of a complicated project, but it is also usually less flexible in changing the direction of research effort and in reaching decisions in general. Occasionally, a promising project will have to be brought to completion as rapidly as possible because of competitive conditions, and in such instances the large organization will have a distinct advantage. This does not mean that the small company should not engage in growth research at all, but it does indicate that the small company must be careful not to engage in a project that may exceed its resources, particularly if the time of completion might be an important factor from a competitive standpoint.

6. *Financial strength.* The magnitude of the research effort, particularly when directed toward diversification, will ultimately determine the magnitude of the capital investment necessary before profits can be realized. This capital investment must be considered in light of the estimated capital requirements of other segments of the business. An intensive search for new supplies of raw materials or major new manufacturing facilities, for example, may be immediately in the offing. There are no generally applicable "rule of thumb" procedures in this area; the judgment of top management, supported by a knowledge of all available facts, is called for.

Another factor to be considered in establishing research objectives is the economic climate—of the world at large, of the United States, and of the particular industry of which the company being considered is a part. Research should not be turned on or off to conform to fluctuations in the economy, but some changes in the selection of new projects in the light of changing business conditions would seem desirable. In a contracting economy, a shift from short-range to intermediate- and long-range projects may be desirable; in an expanding economy, emphasis should probably be given to short-range projects.

Having considered the overall company objectives, the company's assets and liabilities, and the economic climate, the research director is now in a position to establish specific research objectives for the company. Although, ideally, each of these three factors should be in harmony with the research objectives established, a perfect fit is seldom possible in practice.

RESEARCH OBJECTIVES IN SOME TYPICAL INDUSTRIES

We have now reached the point where further broad all-industry generalizations will not be particularly fruitful. Accordingly, let us discuss the development of research objectives for a few typical industries having widely different characteristics. By identifying some of the fundamental characteristics of these industries and relating them to their research objectives, we may provide a basis for applying the various factors involved to other similar industries.

One way of classifying industries is according to general orientation. Since such orientation has a great deal to do with the scope and nature of research activities, this classification would seem to be particularly appropriate for our present uses. Thus, we may consider industries to be oriented toward (1) raw materials, (2) science, (3) markets, or (4) operations.

Raw materials-oriented industries include producers of petroleum, primary metals, inorganic chemicals, and timber products. Companies in such industries generally produce raw materials as an integrated part of their overall operations. They are characterized by high capital investment and low labor costs in relation to product value, the concentration of a large proportion of sales in a few products, and freedom from major product obsolescence in the ordinary sense of the word. Opportunities for logical diversification do exist in these industries, but such diversification does not generally have a major short-range impact upon company affairs. All of these factors result in high technological stability and, in turn, relatively low research expenditures. In such industries, research is largely a defensive tool, and opportunities to use it as an aggressive means of promoting company growth are limited.

Science-oriented industries include those that produce intermediate materials (such as industrial chemicals and plastics) and component parts (particularly those involving the scientific principles of electricity, electronics, mechanics, and hydraulics) for other industries. Companies in such industries are generally characterized by relatively low capital investment and high labor costs in relation to product value, a multiplicity of products, and a moderate product-obsolescence factor. These industries are concerned neither with raw materials supply nor with the requirements of a particular market. Under these conditions, research is directed largely toward product improvement and new product development. The opportunity for diversification is great, and research can be used as an aggressive tool to promote company growth. Research expenditures are generally high, particularly when products important to national defense are involved, and a large part of the research is supported by the Government.

Market-oriented industries include producers of pharmaceuticals, packaged foods, toilet goods, and household appliances. Such industries are characterized by low capital investment and high labor costs in relation to product value, a multiplicity of products, and a high incidence of product obsolescence. Research is largely dictated by consumer wants, and liaison between the marketing and research functions must be extremely close. Although research is directed largely toward new product development, such activity—particularly in the pharmaceutical industry—is likely to be regarded as defensive in nature, since a steady flow of new products must be maintained to replace those that become obsolete.

Operations-oriented industries include the communications, transportation, and public utilities industries. Conditions of complete or partial monopoly, freedom from product obsolescence, and the absence of the factor of product improvement in a physical sense make for extremely high technological stability. Research in such a climate will be of minor importance in the affairs of the company and generally will be directed toward the reduction of costs through the improvement of operations.

Raw materials-oriented industries. The petroleum industry is a good example of raw materials orientation, and a brief description of its research objectives may furnish some guideposts for other industries having a similar orientation.

Maintaining a constant supply of raw materials is probably the most urgent single concern of the petroleum industry today. The cost of petroleum exploration and exploitation is increasing at a faster rate than the general inflation. With an accelerating demand for petroleum, it is inevitable that production and demand curves will eventually cross. Research, however, is postponing the time when this will happen by developing better methods for locating underground structures favorable to the accumulation of petroleum, by developing better methods of recovering petroleum from the earth, and by improving the technology related to the utilization of other raw materials which can be converted to liquid fuels. These alternate raw materials include natural gas, coal, the shale deposits of Colorado, and the Athabasca tar sands of Canada. None of these alternate raw materials is as yet an economic source of liquid fuels, but it seems probable that within a decade or so some of them will be bridging the gap between the supply of natural petroleum and the demand for liquid fuels.

The extent to which any given petroleum company should engage in raw materials research will certainly be influenced by its own position with respect to proven reserves, but there are few companies in a position to maintain an adequate supply in the face of industrywide shortage. In no other aspect of petroleum industry operations is it more important for research to be closely integrated with overall company planning.

The second problem in maintaining today's position is to keep the company's products of marketable quality. The fuels and lubricants of today are vastly different from those of even a decade or two ago. Increases in the compression ratios and speeds of automotive engines and the development of automatic transmissions, faster diesel engines, gas turbines, jet engines, and free-piston engines have placed an ever-increasing burden upon our fuels and lubricants. How does the oil company keep in step with these constant demands for improved quality? Partly by reformulations using available petroleum stocks and additives, partly by changes or improvements in the operation of existing processes, and partly by new installations of existing key processes—but, in the long-range view, largely by the development of completely new processes.

Some of the research activities which are necessary for maintaining competitive product quality include the furnishing of technical service to the marketing department, the evaluation of competitive products, the formulation of new products, and the improvement of existing products through reformulation. If this sounds simple, it should be remembered that a major oil company will generally have more than a thousand products. It is also necessary to keep fully abreast of trends in the design of automobiles, aircraft, and industrial equipment, because changes in the quality of the fuels and lubricants which they will require must be anticipated by at least two years in case new refinery equipment is required.

Research which is directed toward the improvement of individual refinery processes and the correlated operation of all refinery processes is of great importance. Improvement in the operation of a key process, achieved through a better understanding of the operating variables involved or by the removal of bottlenecks which limit capacity, can result not only in decreased production costs but often in the deferral of new capital investments for years and, in the long run, a reduction in the absolute amount of new capital required. In addition to the short-range aspects of refinery planning, research must look years ahead to insure that new facilities are available when increases in product quality or quantity require them.

The last aspect of defensive research is the development of completely new processes. Actually, the development of major new processes may be considered voluntary research, particularly when conducted by companies of less than average size. My reason for saying this is that, in the past, all of those new processes which have had a major impact upon the refining of petroleum have been available for licensing on a reasonable basis— partly, no doubt, because of the very high research and development costs involved and partly because no single company has achieved a dominant patent position.

Once the problems of maintaining a continuing supply of raw materials and insuring the marketability of the company's products have been attended to, the defensive research necessary for maintaining the company's current position has been done. Beyond this, there are two paths to progress: (1) increased volume and (2) new products. While it is entirely possible for a petroleum company to improve its position in its principal products, this will result primarily from factors other than research. On the other hand, the vast opportunities for making chemicals from petroleum are of great interest to the scientist, the research director, and the management of a petroleum company.

During 1962, the production of chemicals from petroleum in the United States was slightly above 70 billion pounds, with a value of close to $9 billion. This represented considerably more than half the value of all chemicals produced, including inorganic chemicals. Several competent authorities estimate that production will increase to more than 100 billion pounds per year by 1967. The fact that petrochemical production has been doubling every five years indicates that these growth estimates may be on the conservative side. Some of the end uses of such chemicals include synthetic fibers and rubbers, plastics, surface coatings, automotive chemicals, nitrogen products, and synthetic detergents. While all of these products have satisfactory growth curves, the potential growth in high-molecular-weight polymers and condensation products is particularly attractive. Another factor which contributes to the attractiveness of petrochemicals is that no shortage of raw materials can be foreseen. At present, only 2 per cent of refinery runs of petroleum are being used for chemical production.

It is certain that much of this chemical growth will result from the use of existing processes to produce existing chemicals. Nevertheless, great opportunities for research exist in the development of new syntheses for established chemicals and in the discovery of new chemicals to satisfy unfilled wants or to improve existing end products. It would be beyond the scope of this paper to describe techniques for the selection of specific research projects; suffice it to say that the ingredients necessary for success are a strong market development group, creative scientists, and a research director who has technical competence, a thorough knowledge of the company's business, and a good measure of plain common sense.

Science-oriented industries. As previously defined, a science-oriented company applies some particular phase of science or technology to the design and production of devices or chemicals which, in general, are either assembled or converted into consumer items by other companies. As an example, we may take a company that produces electronic or electromechanical devices which find their ultimate application in a multitude of consumer products such as automobiles, aircraft, and home appliances. Such a company is also likely to have a great deal of business with the Government in supplying electronic controls for military aircraft, guided missiles, and systems to warn of enemy approach. A company of this type will normally experience rather extreme fluctuations in the market for its products, reflecting ups and downs in the general economy and changing military demands. A prime objective will be to increase civilian business through the introduction of new products into new segments of the economy and thus to lessen the effect of fluctuations in a specific consumer business or in Government demand.

The field of primary interest in this company will probably be the application of electronic controls to any conceivable device or process. Because of the phenomenal growth in the electronics field and the very great potential for future growth, there will be ample room for a company to diversify within its chosen field. The wide application of electronic controls in the automotive, aircraft, missile, and computer fields is well known. Perhaps less well known are the virtually untapped possibilities in the control of industrial processes. A specific example is in the control of atomic reactors for power generation and ship propulsion. Atomic-power generation is approaching commercial significance in Europe and other parts of the world today and is expected to become significant in the United States within a short period of time.

Diversification can be accomplished by the development of new products through a company's own research efforts or by the acquisition of companies with a similar science-based technology but with different markets. Opportunities for such acquisitions are frequent because of the newness of the technology and the fact that many small companies have had their origin in Government research projects.

In such a company, the research function is clearly to develop new products, not only to provide the stabilizing influence previously mentioned but also as an aggressive means of promoting company growth. The more research, the faster the company's growth—but an upper limit commensurate with sound financial considerations must be established. The company must be kept sufficiently liquid to carry it through dips in the general economy and to insure that the research effort is kept reasonably even.

Market-oriented industries. Products from a market-oriented company reach the consumer in the same form in which they leave the factory or plant. Such a company is vitally concerned, therefore, with the factors that cause a consumer to buy an item. Its research objectives include not only problems of achieving proper functioning of a proposed device but problems of styling the ultimate product in such a way that the consumer will choose the company's device over its competitors'. In such companies, research may more properly be termed "development," since the science and technology involved in producing any given device will normally be well established before a market-oriented company becomes concerned with its production. Commonly, a market-oriented company depends upon one or more science-oriented companies for making available the various components of which its consumer product is comprised.

Pharmaceutical companies may be included in the market-oriented category, but they have certain characteristics which distinguish them from companies producing functional consumer items. Consumer appeal in the pharmaceutical trade derives not from gadgetry but from the results of clinical studies and advertising claims based thereon. Research in these companies has a more direct impact upon the consumer and upon the nature of the product offered him. The same necessity exists, however, for determining consumer needs and developing methods of satisfying those needs. The objective of research in such companies is to provide proper functional performance in a chemical rather than a physical sense. This difference accounts for the greater sophistication of the research facilities of pharmaceutical companies as compared with those of other market-oriented companies.

The high mortality rate of pharmaceutical products makes necessary a continuous stream of new products to replace those that become obsolete. Real progress in the biological sciences has just begun. Only recently have we begun to understand the chemistry of living things. The days of bacterial and virus diseases are numbered, and the pharmaceutical companies will play an important role in their demise. Competition will become more fierce and the life span of a new product shorter. Under these conditions, the objective of research should be largely to maintain the company's present market position. Research in its chosen field is so vitally important to such a company that any dilution of effort might result in a serious loss of market position.

The above classification of industries according to basic orientation was made in the hope that some valid rules could be established for each group.

The great differences which exist between industries in each group and the impossibility of satisfactorily classifying many industries, however, have made this hope an illusion. Yet perhaps this attempt at classification has served a useful purpose in emphasizing my original statement that research is not a thing apart.

In any company, the primary research objective should be to establish the technology which the company requires. From a defensive standpoint, this requires a thorough analysis of all phases of the company's business and of the various areas of research involved. Comparison with the research activities of other companies in the same industry is also useful in establishing the level of effort required. The important considerations in establishing research objectives directed toward diversification are an analysis of the strong and weak points of the company with respect to such diversification and a clear understanding of overall company objectives.

EFFECTIVE PLANNING FOR RESEARCH ·

JESSE WERNER

THE BASIC ELEMENTS OF skillful research planning are the same in a small research-based company just starting out to exploit a tiny area of technology as they are in one of the respected giants of American industry. We shall concentrate in this paper on those essential concepts which are the key ingredients of effective research planning for any company.

Research means different things to different people. During the past ten years my firm has made two surveys of the major chemical companies. We asked the participants to list the specific activities that make up research and development as they define it. We found that the lists of no two companies matched exactly. Moreover, several had changed their definitions appreciably during this period. For our present purposes, therefore, we shall define research in the very broad sense as including basic research, laboratory research on new and old products, process development, pilot-plant work, machine design and prototype production, process engineering studies, application research, market research, and market development of new products. Thus, research and development covers all activities from the start of laboratory work on a new product or process until the product is turned over to marketing with established uses and prospective markets outlined and turned over to manufacturing to be handled as a relatively routine production item.

To simplify matters further, we shall limit our consideration to research planning in a medium-size company. This will allow us to examine each of the three basic levels at which such planning must be carried out. In a small company, the same people may carry out several levels of planning. In a large, decentralized company, there will usually be a number of divisions simultaneously planning in different fields and one or more addi-

JESSE WERNER is President, General Aniline & Film Corporation, New York, New York.

tional levels of planning at corporate headquarters. Including these two situations in our discussion would only add complexity and not change any of the fundamentals.

THE LEVELS OF PLANNING

It is perhaps not as well understood as it should be that management is not offered a choice of planning or not planning. The only choice is whether the planning will be orderly and effective or whether it will be haphazard, fragmented, and practically useless.

In the average medium-size company, there are three basic levels of research planning: top management, research management, and the individual researcher or member of the overall research and development team.

If top management is derelict in its planning responsibilities, the second level of management will usually fill the void. Research management will try to compensate, but generally it will find itself in continuous conflict with the managers of production, finance, and marketing. Production will strive to emphasize trouble shooting and product and process improvement. Finance will worry about the cost of research and its effect on profits. Marketing will press for technical services for customers and will often try to extract new products from research before they are really ready. The resulting contest of wills among the several department heads will usually mean that immediate crises are allowed to change the direction of the research program to the detriment of overall needs.

If planning is neglected or not followed through at both of the first two levels, the vacuum will be filled by the third level. Research and development people, in the main, are intelligent and curious. Moreover, they are generally quite industrious. Left to their own devices, they will satisfy their thirst for new knowledge. They will experiment in many directions, each following his own particular bent. Once in a very great while, this leads to a commercially profitable scientific breakthrough, but in most cases it leads up blind alleys, and the company goes absolutely nowhere.

TOP MANAGEMENT'S ROLE

No other top management responsibility is more important than corporate planning. By the same token, it is probably the most exacting and most difficult. Therefore, it is not surprising that it is also the most neglected. Some top executives rationalize this neglect by the claim that it is impossible to plan technological breakthroughs and that therefore it is better to leave this to the ingenuity or accidental discoveries of researchers. Breakthroughs are both hard to plan and rare, but they seem to come much more often to companies that know where they want to go and that establish the right climate for getting there than they do to those companies that are just drifting.

Other top executives believe that their main effort should be devoted to keeping abreast of new developments in their industry and, as soon as these are introduced by their competitors, to rush in and copy or circumvent them. This appears to have all the attractions of easy success, like snatching the brass ring on a merry-go-round and winning a free ride. Although some of this is inevitable in all companies, major emphasis on such procedures will in time lead to second- or third-rate status for a firm. Success belongs, and goes, to the innovators, not the imitators.

Therefore, effective planning for research begins with top management. In fact, effective planning for everything that a corporation does must begin at the top. Problems of finance, acquisitions, production crises, pricing, customer relations, government relations, and so on are often more urgent, more concrete, and more entertaining than the long-range and abstruse problems of research. As a result, research often finds itself the neglected stepchild. Management must keep a proper balance to be truly effective. This is a two-way street: top management must be patient and attentive; research management must be informative, articulate, down to earth, and persistent.

By its nature, research looks to the future. Sales and production, on the other hand, look to the present. Therefore, research planning by top management must be tied to the corporation's long-range thinking. As an effective tool for achieving concrete management planning and for focusing top management's attention on this problem, there is probably no substitute for a formal long-range corporate plan. The preparation and periodic review of such a plan will force the outlining of specific goals in terms of overall growth and direction of growth for the ensuing five-to ten-year period.

Into the preparation of this document should go the best thinking and knowledge available within the company on the general trends of the economy and their effect on the company's business, competitive aspects, obsolescence of the company's product line, and a critical evaluation of the company's strengths and weaknesses. Most important of all, top management must decide where it wants the company to go and, in general, how it plans to get there. Research can help in formulating these decisions. It should not be asked or allowed to make them unilaterally. Once goals are established, research can help to develop feasible means of achieving these goals.

There are usually several ways to reach an objective. This is just as true in business as it is in battle. Let us assume a company has decided to enter an entirely new field. Shall it direct its energies to acquiring an established organization in this field? Shall it try to purchase or license know-how and then build its own business on this basis? Or shall it start from scratch? Again we are faced with a top-level decision, where research management's opinion can be helpful but not necessarily overriding. There are obvious marketing, production, and financial considerations—often far more important than those involving research.

Corporate management must outline the goals and the means of reaching them. In this manner, the research function receives its general assignment and becomes an integral part of overall strategy. Research, by its very nature, implies risk and gives no guarantee of success. Top management must be flexible and patient. However it may appear to the layman and to the writers of Sunday supplements, technological growth and progress involve continuous, unspectacular, hard work. Even major scientific breakthroughs are preceded and followed by years of steady research and development before successful commercial products can be placed on the market. Management must therefore be able to roll with the punch, to make changes where necessary, and to take advantage of favorable situations as they occur.

RESEARCH MANAGEMENT AND THE PLANNING TASK

Within the framework of the corporate goals and areas of activity outlined by top management, research management must carry out the more specific job of its own planning. This is usually a two-part effort. On the one hand, continued research is essential to the production and sale of current product lines. On the other hand, growth also implies the exploration of new areas which will not be reflected in immediate benefits to production and sales.

Research management is called on to exercise simultaneous judgment on these two different aspects. It must make sufficient skilled manpower available to work on specific projects for sales and production in order that both of these operating groups can be assisted effectively in their day-to-day activities. For this purpose, the research director must be flexible in meeting a variety of relatively short-term problems. Not everything desired by the salesmen or the production men can be done within practical budget limitations. The research director must be able to juggle the unlimited demands on his limited manpower in such a way that the immediate profit drive, which these demands represent, is satisfied. This requires a hard-boiled approach toward all such requests and an insistence that they be backed by concrete justifications.

At the same time, the research director must keep patiently and steadily on course with his long-term program. Sales and production will be looking longingly at the manpower committed to new fields and thinking of ways in which it could be better used for their immediate objectives. This he must resist. Moreover, it is an essential part of planning by research management to be self-critical of all long-range research thinking, achievements, and lack of achievements. Periodic soul searching and audits will help prove that these programs are not the whim of the research director but essential and needed for the continued healthy growth of the organization.

Information from continuing market research and market development can be of inestimable value in helping to shape, guide, and change research programs. It can provide clues to competitive activity, applications for new products, customer requirements, and to a recognition of the point where a project has reached a blind alley and should be cut off entirely. Information from these activities and from marketing and manufacturing will aid research management in reorienting its emphasis and reshaping its programs where necessary. Communication must therefore be informal and sincere. Only in this way can research management gain and keep the respect and assistance of other company functions.

It must also have courage. It must fight for the support of those projects that it feels will in the long run help the company reach greater heights. It must also have the courage to stop before it is obvious to everyone else that a project is leading nowhere.

Research management must be alert to what is going on in the rest of the scientific world. It must collect, collate, store, and disseminate facts and information as they become available from the technical literature and from many sources within and without the organization.

Industrial research must be market- and profit-oriented and directed toward achieving corporate ends involving the generation of profits. Therefore, in gauging the technical implications of a program, research management is only carrying out part of its planning job. The concrete realities of customer requirements, market size, share of market, patent position, sales and cost data, production know-how, and capital requirements must all be evaluated along with technical feasibility.

As research results are accumulated, market development will take the new products and subject them to the objective and merciless evaluation of potential customers. Certainly no theories as to potential applications and markets for a product can be as good as the results of actual field trials. Market development and market research are as essential in research planning as providing the manpower and laboratory for carrying out the projects.

THE INDIVIDUAL RESEARCHER'S RESPONSIBILITY

Final work on research planning must be done by the individual researcher or member of the research team. To plan wisely, he needs information and guidelines. Although he is circumscribed by the decisions already made on overall goals and areas of activity by top management and on research project areas by research management, it still remains a fact that a researcher carrying out the actual laboratory work is responsible for his own share of the total planning effort. If he is to do this intelligently, management must see to it that he is provided with the necessary information that will give purpose to his day-to-day activities and their evaluation and interpretation.

He must know what the corporate goals are and how his own project fits into them. Otherwise, he will be working in a vacuum, without incentive and without purpose. He should know why he is being asked to do what he is doing and what will happen when he succeeds. He should be encouraged to communicate with those on his own level and with his supervisors. Not only must he have an attentive and sympathetic ear, but his progress should be reviewed periodically. In this way he will attain the essential habits of planning ahead, of continual review of plans, and of changing them when necessary.

Once the individual researcher has come up with results, the decisions as to which specific paths to pursue for implementation must be made in conjunction with him by research management. When a body of new research information has been assembled which is sufficient for commercial decisions on marketing and production, top management must be ready to step into the picture and make the decisions on finance, manpower, and so forth which will permit implementation of the research results.

Although research can and should be enthusiastic about selling the results of its activities, only management action can effectuate the necessary further steps. Certainly, the planning process is not completed until the decision to commercialize or not commercialize has been made and, if in the affirmative, implemented.

There are a number of additional aspects of research planning: internal organization of research departments, how controls should be exercised through line and functional relations, planning of research budgets, the formal evaluation of research results, the value of cooperative effort with other industrial or Government research laboratories, the use of outside consultants and consulting laboratories. However, the most important aspects of effective planning are those already outlined.

The formula for success in research is relatively simple. First of all, there must be a clear understanding at each level from top management to the individual researcher of the continuous and interlocking responsibilities that exist as regards research planning. Second, goals must be set and kept under constant review in the light of ever-changing facts in order that planning at all levels may be based on realities and not on illusions. Third, there must be patience and consistency, tempered with common sense, to keep working actively toward set goals, even in the face of the reverses inherent in research. Last, but most important, there must be courage to make decisions clearly and cleanly.

SELECTING WORTHWHILE RESEARCH PROJECTS •

GORDON K. TEAL

TEXAS INSTRUMENTS IS A DECENTRALIZED company. It is almost entirely vertically organized; the seven product divisions are independent and in most cases have their own research and development. Within each of the divisions, we have profit centers which are autonomous. This makes for further decentralization and places a large degree of management responsibility near the product and the customer.

Central Research & Engineering has both staff and line functions. It has staff responsibilities for the coordination and integration of the total technical effort of the company. In addition, it has line responsibilities for creating new technology and products in the central research laboratories and for the selection of research projects to bring this technology to fruition.

A primary objective of the central research laboratories is to pace the company's technology—that is, to perform research in areas either more advanced than, or different from, those of the product divisions. The laboratories also perform research in direct support of the divisions when it is considered more practical than for the divisions' R&D groups to perform the research. Funds for our central research laboratories come directly from the office of the president—from corporate funds. This means that in our central research laboratories we have both the obligation and the opportunity, in most cases, to select technical projects which we judge to be best suited to the needs of the company as a whole rather than those which solve specific, short-range, product-department problems. This relative freedom from direct control by the product divisions does not mean that we ignore the specific needs and requests of those divisions

---

GORDON K. TEAL is Assistant Vice President—International Technical Director, Texas Instruments Incorporated, Dallas, Texas.

in our planning. On the contrary, we are in an almost continuous process of presenting our projects and plans to them for criticism. These presentations are essential for maximizing the industrial worth of our research and for insuring an optimum integration of our research with that of the product divisions.

One characteristic of the company has a particularly important influence on the type of research projects which we can select. The areas of technology in which our product divisions are active include geosciences; electronic components, materials, and devices; electronic systems and subsystems; industrial instrumentation and process controls; metals and clad metals; and nuclear fuels. Because we are interested in greatly diversified, high-technology products, our central research laboratories must be science-oriented industrial research centers with broad interests in order to furnish leadership and backup for the product divisions. This orientation attracts scientists who would not be challenged by the thought of making a career of attacking the problem of how to make some product a little cheaper. In fact, one of the achievements of which we are proud is the formation of a competent staff of research personnel with both high academic attainment and creative aptitudes in the central research laboratories.

We define basic research as the search for new phenomena and relationships in nature and applied research as the exploration for and creation of product possibilities out of science and technology. We are excluding development and engineering from our considerations because we assume that when a project reaches the development stage, the worth of the research has already been established. We must remember, however, that basic research, applied research, and development and engineering form a continuum. They are often carried on simultaneously in such a manner as to prevent simple classification of a project. Nevertheless, the criteria for choosing research projects which are predominately basic are generally much different from those used in choosing applied-research projects.

MATCHING RESEARCH TO COMPANY GOALS

The heart of the problem of selecting worthwhile research projects in an industrial laboratory is matching research to company goals. Company goals should take advantage of economic, social, and technological trends and be based on considerations such as management's aspirations and the company's maturity, economic condition, and capabilities in all aspects of creating, making, and selling products. The setting of company goals is a responsibility of top management. Participation in top management planning is essential for the research director because he thereby gains an understanding of company goals and capabilities that cannot be achieved in any other way.

The selection of specific worthwhile research projects is a continuous, full-time activity, in spite of the fact that in most companies there is a specific period set aside each year for presenting research programs to management. At Texas Instruments we formally present short-range plans in December and long-range plans in May. In the course of these planning sessions we submit a compilation of the research projects deemed worthwhile. This compilation consists of projects which were continued and those which were initiated since the last planning session. To be considered worthwhile, a project must have the following general characteristics:

1. It generates good industrial technology.
2. It produces new product ideas or ideas for product improvement.
3. It enhances company prestige in the scientific community.
4. It challenges, extends, and trains technical personnel and project leaders.
5. It has a reasonable probability of success.
6. It has the enthusiastic support of a project manager.

In considering the welfare of the company in the selection of projects, we keep in mind the following points:

1. Company objectives.
2. The nature of the company's present business.
3. The technical prowess of the research personnel.
4. Areas in which the company can market.
5. Products which the company can develop and manufacture.

These considerations are necessary from a business point of view. Our major concerns are whether the company wants and is able to develop, produce, and market the results of a successful project. Although we keep these factors in mind, we have not yet adopted the practice of setting up checklists and grading systems as some companies do. We rely upon our ability to visualize the overall worth of the project. This lack of formality on our part is made up for by the thoroughness with which we prepare for selecting the projects.

THE PROCESS OF SELECTING RESEARCH PROJECTS

In selecting worthwhile research projects, one must decide not only which projects to initiate but also which ones to continue and which ones to drop. In fact, the evaluation of existing projects is probably more important than selecting new projects. It is at least equally important. In addition to the selection of projects, there must also be a decision as to the emphasis to be placed on each project.

Technological forecast. One of the first steps we take in selecting and judging worthwhile projects, whether new or existing, is the preparation of a technological guide or forecast. Areas of technology of interest to the company are selected, and the experts in each area prepare a critique of the state of the art, the trends, the company's competence, what our competitors are doing, and economic opportunities in each area. This guide also serves as a ready reference for both management and technical staff.

Review of product division programs. A continuous review of the research, development and engineering, and marketing programs and plans of the product divisions is an essential and time-consuming activity which must be performed concurrently with the evaluation and selection of research projects. One or two days each month representatives of Central Research & Engineering meet with the directors of the research programs of the product divisions and the central research laboratories to review research activities and plans. We also establish staff groups, when needed in areas of particular interest, to review and propose new plans for specific companywide efforts. In the process of this planning, we get a clear picture of what supporting research will have to be performed by the central research laboratories. Of course, there are frequent *ad hoc* meetings in which we consider our research programs.

Proposal for research projects. While we do not emphasize formality, we have the project managers prepare formal proposals at least once a year for the continuing projects and at the initiation of new projects. The type of information required is shown in Exhibit 1. Both economic and technical data are required. We believe that the research personnel should be aware of the economic aspects of their work from the company point of view. This is an important part of making research worthwhile.

Classification of projects. One of the aids which we have found particularly helpful in evaluating and selecting projects is classifying them according to what I call the "degree of economic confidence," which is the certainty with which the end product or service and resultant billings can be forecast. This classification is also an aid in presentations to management. The need for a classification scheme is particularly apparent when one plans a research program which consists of both long- and short-range projects. Four categories which we have used and found beneficial are: (1) major directed, (2) directed, (3) major exploratory, and (4) long-term exploratory.

Major directed projects have, in general, a high degree of economic confidence. We visualize the end products clearly and are confident that a good market will exist if the project is successful. These projects please

PROJECT PROPOSAL

TITLE:
ANNUAL EXPENDITURE (Est. 1961):
PROFESSIONAL MAN-YEARS (Est. 1961):
PROJECT INITIATED:
TOTAL COST TO DATE:
PRINCIPAL INVESTIGATORS:
PAST ACHIEVEMENTS: ....

....

....

OBJECTIVE AND APPROACH: ....

....

....

CAPITAL EQUIPMENT:

EXPENDITURES: Man-Months/K Dollars

1957:		1961 (Est:		)	(Act:		)
1958:			1st Qtr.	2nd Qtr.	3rd Qtr.	4th Qtr.
1959:		EST.				
1960:		ACT.				

1962	1963	1964	1965	1966	1967	1968	1969	1970	1971

EXHIBIT 1

research directors who not only feel certain of the worth of the projects but know that either central management or a product division agrees with the evaluation. These projects usually receive major emphasis and close attention.

One of the primary tools used in the selection of major directed projects is the *probable-worth analysis,* which is an evaluation of the technical and economic potential, from a business point of view, of a given project. The project manager, with help from specialists in marketing, manufacturing, and finance, prepares the analysis which includes:

1. A discussion of the technological area and the potential technical impact of anticipated research results.
2. A market survey and forecast for similar products.
3. An evaluation of competition in the area.
4. An estimate of the total market for all anticipated products and by-products.
5. An estimate of the market position which the company may cap-

ture, which is based on its expected technological and marketing advantages.

The time period covered by the forecast varies, of course, with the nature of the project, but the analysis is usually projected over a ten-year period. Although we realize full well at this stage that the market estimate is at best an educated guess, we believe in putting actual numbers into the guess in order to visualize the possibilities more accurately.

In addition to the benefits gained in making selections, the probable-worth analysis is a valuable training tool. It provides project managers with a regular opportunity to state their views to management. It serves as a self-correcting guide to the scientific people in their efforts to make a maximum contribution to profits, and it also aids them in communicating their evaluation of the importance of their research to more product- and dollar-minded people in product divisions.

Directed projects are quite similar to major directed projects. Economic confidence in them is high, and the research involved is predominantly applied research. Selection of projects for this category is relatively simple but requires a great deal of discussion with the people in product divisions. The purpose of this type of project usually is to provide specific technology needed in an established product line. In most cases, the product division requests and finances this work and may even manage it. The project manager may be in the division concerned. Although these projects quite often are suggested by the product divisions, technical judgments must come from the research laboratories and, in many cases, from the central research laboratories. Probable-worth analyses are applicable in this category, just as they are in major directed projects.

In the case of the major exploratory projects, where we have a rather clear idea of the potential products or services but lack technology, the technical evaluation becomes more difficult. The purpose of such projects is often to develop technology entirely new to the company. Economic confidence may be relatively low since considerable basic research is usually involved. We know from bitter experience that if the technology which we develop is not the best or the first in its product area, this project may be worth very little to the company. Therefore, we must predict with a high degree of accuracy the quality of technology which will be developed and the probability of solving the technological problem. It turns out, in practice, that major exploratory projects frequently result from our long-term exploratory projects. This means that we have a basis for our judgments. Probable-worth analyses are also frequently applied to projects in this group.

Long-term exploratory projects have the lowest level of economic confidence, and we don't know what the specific product will be. They develop, ultimately, into new major directed projects. The research is predominantly basic in nature, and there is a great deal of freedom permitted the scientists. In general, the scope of an exploratory project is restricted only to the technological areas of present and anticipated major interest to the company. In many cases the selection of a project in this category simply involves the selection of a scientist of high caliber and with interests that parallel those of the company. The degree of freedom permitted the scientist under this type of project is one of the principal factors in attracting and retaining the high-level personnel who contribute so much to the long-range economic success of the company.

Selecting long-term projects is not one of the easier and simpler duties of the research director. He must, through leadership and persuasion, select the mix of projects which through study and intuition he knows will best satisfy the technological needs of the company in both the near and distant future. In a modern industrial corporation the long-range exploratory program is the scientific base of the corporate research activity and is the source of best intelligence for the advancing front of basic knowledge in the external world of science and of the new possibilities opened up. In addition, long-range research provides much of the scientific atmosphere, sets the standards of research excellence, and trains manpower for high-technology development and engineering. Because of the major role of the exploratory program in modern industry, we can readily understand why the research director must place particular emphasis on the selection of projects for this area.

Having specified and defined a project well enough to classify it, one is in a good position to monitor the projects to determine whether to change classification or even drop a project. A major benefit of the classification is that the relative emphasis on basic and applied research becomes apparent. By the way, dropping unproductive projects at early stages is one of the essential steps in selecting worthwhile projects.

EVALUATION OF RESEARCH PROJECTS

How to bring business considerations into the evaluation of a research project is a difficult question. Although we believe that most modern industrial corporations could not long exist in present-day markets without a well-planned research program, we hesitate to place a price tag on a given research project, past or present. In addition to the specific products which come out of them, there are many side benefits. For example, research results from one project can usually be used in many other projects and, not infrequently, in developing industrial processes.

Also, many new ideas and much valuable consulting service come from a good project.

In an attempt to evaluate quantitatively some of our past and present research projects, my company has developed several mathematical models. A simplified version of one of the models used is shown in Exhibit 2. When we analyze a given project using the model, we obtain an *index of research effectiveness*. This index not only includes the dollar value of the project but also establishes the merit of the project from a business viewpoint. The overall measure of the effectiveness of research in a given project consists of four factors: (1) the index of return on research and development, (2) the index of return on assets, (3) the index of dollar volume, and (4) the index of market capture.

The index of return on R&D is net profit during the life of the resulting products (N) divided by 25 times the R&D costs ($25S$). If this index is one, then we can say that there was a satisfactory return on R&D. The factor 25 was taken from the statistics of return on R&D which were collected by the National Science Foundation. In the factor giving the index of return on assets, N is again the net profit during the life of the resulting products, and A is the assets which were required. A return of 13.5 per cent is believed to be a favorable return on assets in a high-technology field where the results are not always assured. To obtain the index for dollar volume, we divided the billings made possible by the product by one twenty-fifth of the total billings during the lifetime of the

INDEX OF RESEARCH EFFECTIVENESS

INDEX OF RETURN ON R&D		INDEX OF RETURN ON ASSETS
$\dfrac{N}{25\,S}$	●	$\dfrac{N}{13.5\%\ A}$
INDEX OF DOLLAR VOLUME		INDEX OF MARKET CAPTURE
$\dfrac{b}{B/25}$	●	$\dfrac{b}{M/2}$

WHERE: N = NET PROFIT
S = R&D COSTS
A = ASSETS REQUIRED
b = TI BILLINGS MADE POSSIBLE
B = TI TOTAL BILLINGS
M = TOTAL AVAILABLE MARKET

EXHIBIT 2

product. In other words, a worthwhile project should make possible a 4 per cent increase in annual total billings. In the case of the index of market capture, we say, in effect, that a product which will capture one half of the total available market is worthwhile. If, when we multiply these four indices, we obtain a factor of one or more, we should indeed have a worthwhile project. This is the index of research effectiveness in its simplest form; the index includes only the direct and obvious returns from a research project.

OUTLINING THE PROBLEM

The selection of worthwhile research projects for a growth industry is a continuous but rewarding problem. It requires the services of a research director with an overall understanding of the state of the art, the trends, and the scientific disciplines involved and also one who is well informed on his company's objectives. Although the problem is the direct responsibility of the research director, others in top management must contribute to the solution. Members of the technical staff of the laboratories must also participate, since the selection of a specific project is the matching of the technical personnel, technological opportunities, and company objectives.

The research director must understand scientists as well as science and have the managerial fortitude to say yes or no at the appropriate times or to adjust the research effort to the situation. The research director must consider both the long- and short-range goals of the company. This means that he must develop a well-balanced program which includes the appropriate percentages of both basic and applied research and the proper mix of short-term and long-term projects. For research to pay off, the overall program must always contain a selected percentage of laboratory personnel allotted to projects for which the products are clearly in mind. The remaining personnel should be assigned to exploratory projects where greater understanding and technology are the principal objectives.

More and more managers are asking if research pays off—if it carries its own weight. Every research director should be expected to answer these questions and should prepare for them by documenting the many contributions of his laboratory. Of course, some of the contributions of research are intangible, but worthwhile research projects will yield many results that are very tangible. In short, worthwhile research projects are those which motivate research people to do the future research of the company and which show promise of meeting the company's economic goals.

ORGANIZATION

RESEARCH ORGANIZATION:
CENTRALIZED VERSUS DECENTRALIZED •

RICHARD O. ROBLIN

Until recently industrial research, while accepted as a potential contributor to the growth and prosperity of a progressive business enterprise, was still regarded as a thing apart from the mainstream. Scientists were not expected to be particularly knowledgeable about such matters as profit margins or market potentials. They were looked upon by their nontechnical associates as being somehow different and unworldly.

As technological developments became increasingly important in many industries, the need for efficient organization of research became more apparent. In addition, such factors as rapidly increasing costs, lower productivity of research, greater competition for manpower and results, as well as Government contracts, and the increasing importance of new products—all contributed to a more active concern for the efficient operation of research and development activities. As a result, industrial research has now become as much an integrated function of many large companies as sales, production, or finance.

While research people desired a greater voice in management during this evolutionary process, many of them were not adequately prepared to accept the challenge when it arrived. Their nontechnical associates spoke a different language: one which they understood only vaguely. Fortunately, recognition of this problem has led to a process of mutual education. Technical staffs are being informed about the problems and objectives of the business enterprise. They are now aware of such things as the relative profit margins of various product lines. In turn, research programs and progress have become a more vital concern of the sales and manufac-

RICHARD O. ROBLIN is Vice President—Research, Commercial Development, and Engineering and Construction, American Cyanamid Company, Wayne, New Jersey.

turing departments. Cross-fertilization through transfer of personnel from one function to another has been a particularly useful device in furthering this process of mutual education.

In the past decade American Cyanamid Company has come full circle in the organization of its research and development activities. Prior to 1954 these functions were largely decentralized and loosely coordinated. Each group went its own separate way with little concern about what was happening at other laboratories. Pharmaceutical research, for example, was conducted at three different locations by groups whose communications were on an informal and sporadic basis. Overlapping projects were not uncommon. In some cases this duplication led to stimulating and effective internal competition. However, in other cases the results were less favorable; and since few companies can afford such a luxury, the situation had to be resolved. Consequently, the decision was made to centralize all research and development.

This step led to the gradual elimination of duplication of research programs and to the consolidation of the work in areas such as pharmaceuticals in one location. In retrospect, the pooling of all research in one large division paid other dividends. Scientists became better acquainted with one another through frequent meetings and conferences. It also engendered a cooperative spirit, previously lacking, which persists even today.

But the centralized system presented some problems of its own. For despite the appointment of a technical liaison man from the centralized research division for each operating division, the relationship was far from satisfactory. General managers of the operating divisions no longer felt any direct responsibility for R&D even though they participated in the formulation of their research programs and even though they were charged for them.

It soon became apparent that the missing ingredient in centralized research was commercial guidance. Without day-to-day contact, research became more isolated from the realities of the marketplace. Researchers were asked to establish market potentials for various products without the aid of sound commercial intelligence. As a result, research projects of a long-range or fundamental nature, which were uninhibited by these considerations, became more popular. But such projects did not arouse the interest or enthusiasm of the operating divisions; new products languished or gained acceptance much too slowly.

These and other factors finally led to the return of the R&D function to the operating divisions. The major consideration in this move was the fact that division managers were responsible for both the current and future operations of their units. If research and development has become a prime function in a progressive business enterprise, then divisional managers must have control of it. The alternative is that they should not be held responsible for the future growth of their divisions.

The return of this responsibility to the operating divisions left a nucleus of longer-range research groups which could explore new areas for the company. These groups were reorganized and consolidated to form a corporate Central Research Division with headquarters at the company's Stamford, Connecticut, laboratories. This Division also currently serves as the host laboratory for certain operating divisions and provides research services, maintenance, and other facilities.

At present there are ten operating divisions carrying on their own research and development in a number of major laboratories:

1. Agricultural Division; Princeton, New Jersey.
2. Building Products Division; Sanford, Maine.
3. Davis & Geck Division; Danbury, Connecticut.
4. Fibers Division; Stamford, Connecticut, and Santa Rosa, Florida.
5. Formica Corporation; Evendale, Ohio, and Stamford, Connecticut.
6. Industrial Chemicals Division; Stamford, Connecticut.
7. Lederle Laboratories Division; Pearl River, New York.
8. Organic Chemicals Division; Bound Brook, New Jersey, and Stamford, Connecticut.
9. Pigments Division; Bound Brook, New Jersey, and Piney River, Virginia.
10. Plastics and Resins Division; Stamford and Wallingford, Connecticut.

Each of these divisions now has its own director of research or technical director, who is a member of the management team. Thus he not only is familiar with the commercial activities of the division but participates in its management decisions. His position is comparable to the sales manager or the manager of manufacturing.

Technical liaison among the operating divisions as well as the Central Research Division is formalized through a Research Coordinating Committee, composed of all the divisional technical directors together with the vice president for research. Its primary function is communications, although various subjects of interest to research management are discussed. Throughout the year, at the committee's monthly meetings, each research director has an opportunity to review his program.

An annual technical conference provides another occasion for many research and development people in the various divisions to become better acquainted with major projects of companywide importance. These conferences were initiated when operations were centralized and have been continued to help maintain the close relationships developed at that time.

During 1963 Cyanamid will spend approximately 5 per cent of its total sales, roughly $35 million, for R&D, excluding Government contracts. Of this amount, 85 per cent is spent by the operating divisions, and the remainder by Central Research.

The present Central Research Division is comprised of four departments which, partly for historical reasons and partly for lack of better terms, are called the Applied, Chemical, Contract, and Physical Research Departments. About 75 per cent of the work of these departments is directed toward products and markets which are new to Cyanamid. The remainder is called "science-oriented" research since it is not directed toward any specific new product or process. In addition, the division is also responsible for the operation of the Cyanamid European Research Institute in Geneva, Switzerland, whose work is also science-oriented.

The Applied Research Department primarily handles projects which are close to potential commercialization and frequently takes them over from the Chemical or Physical Research Departments. However, a considerable amount of fundamental work goes right along with Applied's use-oriented projects. This department, as well as others in Central Research, also carries out projects sponsored and paid for by the operating divisions. This research usually involves specialized equipment or unique talents not available elsewhere in the company.

In contrast to the other departments, no science-oriented work is carried out by the Applied Research Department. The programs of both the Chemical and Physical Research Departments provide a balance between science- and use-oriented projects of a longer-rate nature. The use of these terms has helped to overcome the time-honored arguments about basic or fundamental research versus applied research. We believe that use-oriented projects frequently require basic research which may be more demanding than that encountered in science-oriented fields.

While not all Government-contract research is handled by the Contract Research Department, this group carries out several of the largest ones. It also provides one of the chief liaisons with the various Governmental agencies. When a contract fits more naturally into one of the other departments or an operating division, it is carried out by the most logical group. However, Contract Research provides assistance to other groups in drawing up contract proposals.

While Government contracts are sought in certain areas, they are limited to those in which we have a commercial interest as well, or to those in which we may be able to make an important contribution to national defense. All told, they account for from 5 to 10 per cent of the total company R&D budget at present.

The general manager of the Central Research Division reports to a vice president who also has a staff relationship to the research being carried out in the operating divisions. Also reporting to this vice president are the general managers of the Commercial Development Division and the Engineering and Construction Division.

One of the most important functions of the Commercial Development Division, which includes both market research and market development activities, is to provide guidance for the Central Research Division. Every use-oriented project has both a market researcher and a market development man following it closely. A number of these projects are budgeted by the Commercial Development Division and paid for by that division. While this is simply a different corporate pocket, the purpose is to obtain maximum cooperation between this division and Central Research.

Initial sales of new products are handled by the Market Development Department. These new products are not turned over to an operating division until they have passed the twin tests of market acceptance and profitability. By then it is rarely difficult to find a warm reception for them. In the interim, initial production and sales are handled by the Commercial Development Division.

In a highly diversified company such as Cyanamid, finding new and promising research projects is not an easy job. Wherever possible, the market potentials and chances of commercial success, along with the technical problems, are evaluated jointly by the Research and Commercial Development Divisions before any laboratory work is undertaken on a new project.

Once work is initiated, it is reviewed regularly by members of both divisions. Target dates are established for all the use-oriented projects. These constant reviews help generate a feeling of urgency and keep the projects moving along.

The present R&D organization of American Cyanamid Company has been in effect for about three years. That's probably not long enough to establish all its strong and weak points. But our feeling—even though based on this short experience—is that for a large divisionalized company our present organization seems to have more merits than shortcomings. Such an organization would obviously not fit a highly centralized business enterprise. It presents problems of communication for any company which require continual attention.

No form of organization can substitute for good people, but a poor organization can make life unnecessarily complicated for them. Able scientists, sound projects, and proper guidance are probably all more important than the particular type of research organization. But with increasing competition and the rising cost of research, it is simply good sense to try to establish the most effective organization: one that will provide the public and the company with the earliest benefits of the fruits of research.

PROGRESS THROUGH COORDINATED EFFORT •

PAUL L. SALZBERG

O RGANIZED INDUSTRIAL RESEARCH has become a vital factor in the nation's economy and is an essential activity in many industries. It provides insurance against obsolescence and a basis for diversification through the development of new products and processes. However, research alone cannot accomplish these objectives—it is just one member of the team. Only through the coordinated efforts of research, engineering, manufacturing, and sales—backed up by a research-minded top management—can the results of research be put to useful purpose. Research has therefore become an integral part of the operations of many companies.

The term "research" is currently used by various organizations to cover a great diversity of scientific, engineering, and development activities. In Du Pont, research has been defined as "critical investigations in the physical and natural sciences directed toward the discovery of new knowledge." The program embraces pioneering research aimed at new ventures and research in support of present lines of business. The overall program has for many years included fundamental research which is carried out for the advancement of scientific knowledge in fields of present or potential interest to Du Pont without regard to specific commercial objectives. Fundamental research was started in Du Pont on a formal basis in 1927 and has become an important activity in the company's research divisions. It has proved very fruitful in laying the foundation for applied research. It has been a key factor in shaping the business of the company as it exists today.

Patent activities in the Du Pont Company are carried forward in close cooperation with our research program. Were it not for the prospect of

PAUL L. SALZBERG is Director, Central Research Department, E. I. du Pont de Nemours & Company, Wilmington, Delaware.

obtaining strong patent protection, industry would not be justified in undertaking many costly research programs aimed at the invention of new products and processes. But patents have an even greater significance than the mere granting of protection to inventors. They are, in essence, agreements between inventors and the public, and they serve two vital purposes: (1) they stimulate invention and discovery and thereby encourage the development of new products and (2) they make it possible for inventors to disclose their inventions to the public instead of keeping them secret. Permanent secrecy on industrial technology would greatly stifle progress and suppress the flow of new knowledge through publications by scientists in industry. We therefore consider it essential to carry forward a patent program closely coordinated with research and to have technical personnel within the research organization work closely with patent attorneys.

REFLECTION OF DECENTRALIZED PATTERN

The organization of Du Pont research follows the decentralized pattern of the company (see Exhibit 1). Research is carried on by the manufacturing departments and also by auxiliary departments which conduct it for the benefit of the company generally and for individual manufacturing departments. We have, therefore, research units in many departments, with the result that different points of view are brought to bear on the company's research objectives.

Executive and Finance Committees exercise control of the company's overall research expenditures through authorization of annual budgets submitted by the individual departments. There is no general research budget. The forecast of expenditure in this area is, therefore, merely the sum of the separate departmental budgets. For the information and guidance of the Executive Committee, the departmental research budgets are supported by a report presenting the previous year's accomplishments and outlining the expected trends in the forthcoming research program. Furthermore, a member of the Executive Committee is given the responsibility of acting as adviser on research to all departments.

Each of the domestic manufacturing departments has its own research division charged with the responsibility of carrying out the research necessary for the continuance and further development of the department's business. The research directors are on the same organizational level as the directors of manufacturing and sales. Each department formulates its own research program along those lines which seem best in the opinion of its management.

As to the auxiliary departments, the Engineering Research Laboratory investigates unit operations of chemical engineering, materials of construc-

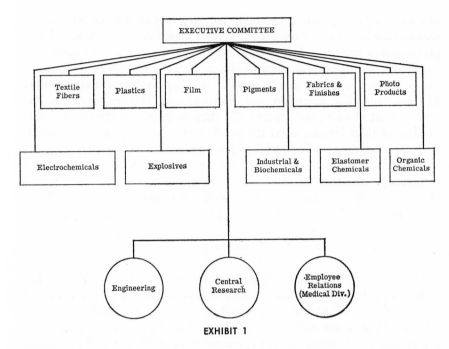

EXHIBIT 1

tion, and methods for measuring and controlling chemical reactions. The Engineering Department operates three other laboratories. The Radiation Physics Laboratory conducts research on the interaction of high-energy radiation and matter. The Mechanical Research Laboratory is active in such fields as applied mechanics, precision measurement and finishing, wear and friction, and electro-mechanical research and has as its objective the development of mechanical equipment for special operations engaged in by the company.

The Employee Relations Department, through its Medical Division, directs the Haskell Laboratory for Toxicology and Industrial Medicine. This laboratory is devoted to industrial medical investigations that will reveal, at a very early stage, physiological changes which may be caused by the action of chemical compounds. The objectives are to set up adequate measures to protect employees within the plants and instruct consumers on the safe handling of Du Pont products.

The Central Research Department is engaged in fundamental and long-range research to help provide the foundations for new developments in future years. Over half of the Central Research Department's expenditures are authorized directly by the Executive Committee in order to provide latitude for the exploration of entirely new fields not connected with present manufacturing interests. The remainder of the Central Research Department's work is sponsored by individual manufacturing departments and helps to bridge the gap between the new discoveries in pioneering research and the application of these discoveries to the development of new products and processes. Futhermore, sponsored research in the Central Research Department often provides a fresh approach to long-range research objectives in the industrial departments.

MOVEMENTS OF A TYPICAL PROJECT

Because it involved the coordinated efforts of many Du Pont research divisions, the development of nylon and other linear condensation polymers is an outstanding example of the way in which a research project progresses through the organization.

Fundamental research in the Central Research Department resulted in discovery of the broad class of linear condensation polymers having a crystalline structure. When it was discovered that these condensation polymers could be spun into fibers and oriented by stretching to induce remarkable properties, the Textile Fibers Department supported research in the Central Research Department and also initiated work in its own laboratories. A polyamide called nylon 66 was selected for initial commercialization. Furthermore, the Plastics Department initiated production of nylon bristle and molding powder based on its experience in the plastics field. Concurrently, the same department undertook the development of processes for manufacturing nylon intermediates from petroleum or coal. Substantial contributions were made by the Engineering Department in processing equipment, by the Haskell Laboratory on the toxicology of intermediates, and by the Organic Chemicals Department on dyes and finishes.

The broad concept of crystalline condensation polymers fostered many new lines of pioneering research throughout the company's research divisions. It provided the foundation for the subsequent development of polyester fibers by the Textile Fibers Department, polyester transparent film by the Film Department, and polyester photographic film base by the Photo Products Department. The Explosives Department carried out research on intermediates which led to the production of terephthalic acid for polyesters.

During the course of the fundamental research program on condensation polymers and their intermediates, it was found that polyisocyanates could be used for cross-linking and chain-extending molecules in a great variety of combinations. The Elastomer Chemicals Department has applied this new knowledge in chemistry in the development of new elastomers, adhesives, and foams.

RELIANCE ON HIGH-CALIBER PERSONNEL

It is apparent that the diversity of interests and technology in the company's separate research organizations was an important factor in capitalizing on the discovery of a new class of polymers arising from fundamental research. However, a research organization is obviously no better than the individual men who carry out the research in the laboratory. We therefore attach great importance to obtaining the most highly qualified technical men, particularly scientists capable of doing independent creative research. The recruiting of top-flight men is a major responsibility of management.

But recruiting is only a start. The research scientist must be provided with an environment that will stimulate his best efforts. He is encouraged to use his creative ability to the fullest extent in prosecuting his own problems and in suggesting new lines of research. He is encouraged to publish research results of high scientific caliber after steps have been taken to obtain appropriate patent protection.

It is important to have a salary policy which rewards the research man for his efforts irrespective of the commercial outcome of his work. Such a policy permits advancement for the career scientists as well as for those who fill executive positions. If a man's interests and talents remain in laboratory work, he can still progress in salary, responsibility, and scientific stature. On the other hand, many executive and management positions in the company are occupied by technical men who started their careers in research.

Extensive facilities and services must be provided for the research man in order that he may use his time most efficiently and concentrate on the technical aspects of his program. The Experimental Station, as a geographical site for laboratories of 12 separate departments, makes it possible to provide more extensive services than could be justified in each separate location. Exhibit 2, illustrating the kinds of aids to the research man provided at the Experimental Station, may be visualized as an organization chart from his viewpoint. As shown, these aids include the library staff, laboratory technicians, mechanics and electricians, glass blowers, and instrument makers.

PROVISION FOR THE EXCHANGE OF INFORMATION

An important activity in an industrial research organization is the provision of personnel and facilities for handling and disseminating the ever-increasing flow of published technical information in journals and patents. As an integral part of its research facilities, Du Pont maintains

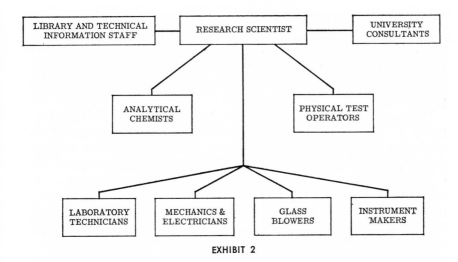

| LIBRARY AND TECHNICAL INFORMATION STAFF | RESEARCH SCIENTIST | UNIVERSITY CONSULTANTS |

| ANALYTICAL CHEMISTS | PHYSICAL TEST OPERATORS |

| LABORATORY TECHNICIANS | MECHANICS & ELECTRICIANS | GLASS BLOWERS | INSTRUMENT MAKERS |

EXHIBIT 2

libraries at each of the company's major research laboratories. The Lavoisier Library at the Experimental Station houses approximately 50,000 books and bound journals and an extensive collection of pamphlets and patents. It regularly receives some 1,100 technical periodicals and journals. A special technical staff makes translations, literature surveys, and patent searches to assist and guide research. Bulletins covering abstracts of technical articles and patents are issued weekly to research personnel of the company in order to disseminate this new information as promptly as possible.

A number of outstanding academic scientists are retained as consultants in order to bring new viewpoints to bear on the company's research program. These men constitute a bond between the academic world and the industrial laboratories and help our research men to keep abreast of trends in academic research.

Communications are of vital importance in a company carrying out diversified research in many separate laboratories. It frequently happens that research under way in one field can provide new technical information which will result in an important contribution to a wholly unrelated line of research. The usual methods for exchanging information through the medium of reports and formal reviews serve an important purpose, but perhaps the most effective methods for exchanging information are those which depend upon personal contacts. It is important that the exchange of information be promoted at all levels in the research organizations.

The research directors of the company, as well as laboratory directors at the Experimental Station, hold informal luncheon discussions periodically, at which time new technical information is discussed as well as matters dealing with the administration of research. Scientific symposiums are held at the Experimental Station on subjects of broad interest to the company and are attended by representatives of all departments having an interest in the field under discussion. At these symposiums, Du Pont research scientists present papers covering their own work, and time is provided for audience participation.

Perhaps the most widely used method for exchanging research information is the day-to-day contact among research people. This is one of the reasons for having 12 departments of the company represented by research groups at the Experimental Station. In this area we have about 1,200 technical personnel trained in more than 200 different universities and colleges and representing a broad spectrum of science and engineering. It may well happen that knowledge of a new discovery is first exchanged through informal discussions among the scientists at the Experimental Station.

* * *

It should be emphasized that there are many different types of research organizations possible, depending upon the particular needs and background of the company involved. However, in the last analysis the success of the research effort of a company will depend on the creativeness and skill of the individual men engaged in the research.

ORGANIZING RESEARCH IN

A GROWTH INDUSTRY •

WILLIAM P. GAGE

THE W. R. GRACE & COMPANY HAS GROWN rapidly in chemicals, both by mergers and by growth from within. A discussion of the problems posed in organizing research in a short time under the involved conditions imposed may add something of interest and use to the literature on organizing the research program.

In 1956 our president, J. Peter Grace, gave a talk before the Industrial Economic Conference sponsored by the Stanford Research Institute. In it he showed what the company was faced with in its growth plan for the future:

> When the present management entered in 1945, it followed the custom of the House and took a long, hard look at what we had, and this is what we saw:

> The net fixed assets of the firm were 61% in the steamship business; 32% in Latin American industrial and commercial activities; and 7% in various domestic businesses in the United States, in addition to our interests in the Grace National Bank and the Pan American-Grace Airways.

The company lacked participation in growth industries in the United States; we made exhaustive studies during the next few years and came to the conclusion that the chemical industry in this country had the greatest growth potential of the major segments of industry. So our efforts were directed toward entering this field as soon as possible.

We began in 1952 with the organization of the Grace Chemical Company, which was to build and operate an ammonia and urea plant at Memphis, Tennessee, and which constituted our research and development

WILLIAM P. GAGE is Senior Vice President, Chemical Group, W. R. Grace & Company, New York, New York.

personnel, although up to this time we had no laboratories or research program other than the study and investigation of fields that showed growth opportunities and of chemical companies that would be attractive acquisitions.

In 1952, Grace Chemical Company licensed processes which enabled it to start construction of the ammonia and urea plant in Memphis. During 1954 we merged with two well-known chemical companies: Davison Chemical Company—prominent in inorganic chemicals, fertilizers, and catalysts—and Dewey and Almy Chemical Company—equally versed on the organic side in chemical specialties, complex polymeric compounds for container sealing, synthetic rubber latices, and polymers such as CRYOVAC film for packaging.

While we were getting acquainted with these acquisitions, we brought our Memphis plant on stream. Some time later Grace Chemical was split, the name being kept by the operating division and the Research and Development segment becoming the Grace Research and Development Division.

Subsequently, another decision of great importance to Grace's chemical future was taken. This was to enter the field of bulk polymers—particularly polyolefins. As the first step, a license was taken from Phillips for high density polyethylene, and construction was started on a plant at Baton Rouge, Louisiana.

This decision naturally had a profound effect on our research planning and accelerated action toward a central research laboratory. While the polyethylene plant was being built, another operating division, known as Polymer Chemicals, was split off to carry on the bulk polymer segment of our chemical business.

Our earliest thoughts on research were quite humorous in retrospect. Can you imagine a management trying to decide on a research budget amounting to millions of dollars when before 1950 the board had never authorized a plant costing more than $2 million? The story of the education of a nontechnical management in the idea that it must add millions to its thinking about budgeting requirements for research could make a book in itself. It wasn't until Grace had acquired two chemical companies with long years of experience in research programs of their own that any real headway was made.

Perhaps one of the greatest breakthroughs in the thinking on why we should have central research is embodied in a memo presented to our top management late in 1954:

> Everyone seems to be in agreement that we will eventually need a central laboratory to do the more fundamental, exploratory research on new products or in new fields not already exploited by one of the operating divisions. This laboratory must be free from the daily pressures of the operating

groups who frequently are too concerned with the problems of today to have much sympathy with the dreams of tomorrow.

If we are going to go after the maximum dollar return on the capital and research investment, it is axiomatic that we will have to do more than rely on growth by methods such as expansion of present or allied product lines, or buying the know-how for "standard" processes, or purchase of established chemical companies. In addition, it will be necessary to develop new products or processes, or to acquire them while they are still in a formative or unproven stage. The latter type of exploratory and developmental activity is a function of the corporation rather than an operating division.

We must recognize at the outset that the setting up of a central laboratory is not an automatic guarantee of a successful research or development program. Assuming technical competence, its success is a combination of the choice of problems selected and of consistency in top management in not arbitrarily shifting signals with respect to problems under investigation. If this new group is to get a good start in the company, they must come in to a job which needs to be done and in which they can make a tangible contribution by their creativeness. We can't bring in qualified technical people and just let them mill around.

In order to insure continued profitable operation and growth of our present divisions, we believe they should maintain laboratories of their own, capable of:
  (a) Providing technical service to customers.
  (b) Solving the technical problems of the factories.
  (c) Improving existing products and processes to maintain or improve quality and reduce cost.
  (d) Developing new products allied to existing product lines.

The central laboratory should do exploratory research in the specific fields outside of this area but in which the management feels there is opportunity.

Our ideas on the function of our central research laboratory as formulated five years ago were as follows:

1. Serve as a long-range research group, concentrating in fields that the company believes may be attractive to it.

2. Serve as a centralized facility for specialized services to the divisions of the company.

3. Serve as a research and development group to enable Grace to profit from new ideas brought to it.

4. Serve as a technical consulting group to the Grace management for suggesting possible new developments that might be profitable and aiding the management in the technical aspects of its decisions.

5. Do research for the company divisions on a contract or annual budget basis if requested.

Our management by this time had added not only over a $100 million in chemical assets but, equally as important in its pattern for growth in the chemical industry, it had added men of chemical stature to its board of directors, and this helped round out our newly emerging chemical image.

Our next move was to find a site for our central research facilities that would be located in an area that would allow for detached creative thinking and yet be convenient enough to attract top-flight personnel who would find not only adequate housing but opportunities to meet and exchange ideas with other scientific personnel from laboratories in surrounding areas. If I may be permitted a slight humorous reminiscence, we soon found that every director is an expert on where to put a research laboratory, and I'm sure we could publish a book called "Finding the Ideal Location."

We studied locations while gradually acquiring a nucleus of research management personnel whose backgrounds were in line with the interests of our existing chemical divisions. We drew up plans for a laboratory and were ready to start construction as soon as the "ideal" location could be decided upon. While this was going on, our Davison Division was building its new research facilities near Clarksville, Maryland, which is located less than an hour by car from Baltimore and Washington.

At this point, the Davison management made us an offer. They would be willing to turn over their new laboratory and all of its personnel to the Grace Research Division and then contract with it for all of their future research. Their site had ample acreage for expansion and for the new central research laboratory.

In a matter of days, our management approved the idea, and the plan was executed exactly as it was conceived. During 1957—while our inorganic, catalyst, and agricultural chemicals laboratory was being completed —construction was started on an adjacent laboratory which would house our organic, polymer, and research-services groups. Today we have over $8 million dollars invested in these facilities.

A director of research is responsible for the overall research effort. Reporting to him are research directors for each department representing organic chemistry, polymer research, research services (which consists of all the highly specialized instruments for emission, absorption, and mass spectroscopy, chromatography, and electron-beam radiation), inorganic, catalyst, and agricultural chemistry.

Grace has some departments that are not always found in a research organization, including a Process Engineering Department which handles chemical engineering process design of plants, studies and evaluates new processes, and selects the best process for commercialization by our divisions. We also have a Patent Department located in the laboratory close to the research chemists.

We have been in operation with the present facilities and people for five years at our Washington Research Center. During this time, our research organization thinking has matured rapidly. The Research Division has recently been given cognizance over the research conducted by the divisions themselves, which is largely applied and fairly short term and within the fields of activity of the divisions or closely allied fields. To be sure that the best research skills and equipment are applied to all problems within Grace, we have an active Research Committee. It is made up of the research directors of all of the divisions, and the senior vice president, chemicals is its chairman. Meetings are held usually at different plant locations each month or so in order to bring our personnel into closer understanding of the applied problems at an operating level. We achieve greater understanding at these meetings and a cross-fertilization of ideas.

Hardly a day passes at the Washington Research Center without a visitor from one of our operating divisions. This, of course, brings us closer to all kinds of problems whether they are in the sales or marketing or commercial development stages. We encourage these visitors because they help us interpret the objectives and desires of the management of the divisions and allow the reappraisal of our short- and long-term goals on an active and commercial basis.

It is my belief that one specific research objective is to sustain and extend the present business of the company. Industrial research is generally done to maintain and improve the profit-making ability of a company. The chemical industry is fast-moving and dynamic; and competition in profitable fields is becoming more and more intense.

If a company currently enjoys an unusually favorable position with a given product or product line in a particular field, this company immediately becomes the envy of potential competitors who either initiate new research or intensify old research in an attempt to obtain a part of the attractive business. Because of this competitive situation, every successful company must devote a substantial part of available research resources just to maintain a current profitable business in relation to its competitors. This involves spending money and utilizing research people to develop new facts about old products and to find new ways to utilize old products. Frequent re-evaluation of the technical foundation upon which the current business exists is necessary. Research for the benefit of existing products must cover every aspect of producing and selling the product. Raw materials, quality and prices, shipping costs, plant investment and obsolescence, efficiency of operation, and product quality are but a few of the critical and constantly changing aspects associated with all existing products. No matter what the objective may be, its outcome depends to a large extent on the creativity of the men who carry out the research program.

When we took over the laboratories of the Davison Division, we already had a program built up over the years based on the needs and objectives of Davison itself. In building a staff for our organic and polymer research program, we selected men with years of experience in this field and indoctrinated them in what we believe to be the areas of future growth in our company. By introducing these men to every aspect of our company, we were able to provide the type of staff required for the laboratories. The selection of these men was left to research rather than the personnel department. It takes a top research man to interview and hire a Ph.D out of the university, because these men are placed on a common meeting ground of research evaluation and interest. I believe the teams we have built up by this method are of a high caliber and are already producing results.

Grace has organized a flexible functional program not to impress stockholders or investment analysts but to produce areas of growth in the products we make today and to provide the guidepost for our expansion tomorrow.

We have expanded rapidly into the chemical industry; today our net fixed assets at the end of 1962 were 48 per cent in the chemical business, which was only a gleam in the eye of management 11 years earlier; 19 per cent in the steamship business in contrast to 61 per cent 17 years earlier; 12 per cent in Latin American operations, contrasted with 32 per cent in the 1945 figures; while our general United States business is only 2 per cent in contrast to the 7 per cent of 1945. Although the 19 per cent in steamships as contrasted with the former 61 per cent seems much lower, actually 19 per cent today is a net increase of $42.5 million in assets over 1945— or twice as much. The same is true of our foreign business. In reality, the investment is up about 300 per cent over 1945.

Our chemical investments have also amounted to an education into the appropriate size and scope of an adequate research organization and a budget to operate this organization. In 1963 we budgeted over $11 million for central and divisional research which is based on a percentage of chemical sales. This figure includes market research and general market studies, technical service, capitalizable engineering, quality control, and product testing.

These words will attest to the fact that we believe research to be of greatest importance to our continued growth and in remaining competitive in the new chemical world that is looming even larger on our horizon. Organizing the research program takes time, patience, and education— not only of management but of all concerned. The first thing a company must do is to know its corporate objectives and then develop a long-range plan that management is willing to adhere to over a span of years. Success in research depends on many factors, but as some wise sage has said, "You can't beat a man with a plan!"

TECHNIQUES FOR UTILIZING RESEARCH •

JOHN A. FIELD

T HE WORLD OF TODAY IS VASTLY different from the world in which we lived a few years ago. Automobiles, aircraft, radios and television, electronic computers, electric refrigerators, and many other technological developments have changed our lives immeasurably. This fact has been often mentioned, but it is well to point out that none of these developments would have materialized if someone had not been able to translate an original discovery into practical terms to fill a need—either of man or of industry.

In the past 40 years, research expenditures have increased in this country from $29.5 million to $10.6 billion a year. Of even greater significance is the fact that, of all the money spent for research and development since 1920, more than half has been spent since 1956. It can be reasonably assumed that this expansion of effort will continue to increase the rate of scientific discovery in the country by leaps and bounds.

A very real problem then arises: how to utilize the new discoveries most efficiently. This is not only an industrial problem but also a national problem, as the competition in space technology has so clearly emphasized. In order to capitalize on the opportunities afforded us by research discoveries, it is imperative that we devise faster and more efficient ways to translate such discoveries into usefulness.

We must not waste the exquisite research mechanism that American industry has put together. How can we make certain, for example, that when compound X or principle Y is discovered in one of our labs, it will not lie unused because no practical applications come immediately to mind? Or, to take another example, how can we be sure that the time

JOHN A. FIELD is Vice President, Union Carbide Chemicals Company, New York, New York.

and money devoted to inefficient administrative procedure may not prevent us from taking advantage of the productive results of the laboratories?

In considering this problem, it is helpful if we limit the discussion to discoveries which have clearly shown promise for commercial realization. Our problem, basically, is how to capitalize on breakthrough.

The job of translating a scientific breakthrough into a salable product requires hard work. We cannot rely on chance alone, and we cannot assume that the world is just waiting for our particular discovery. Michael Faraday was once questioned by a legislator about the practical applications of his theories of electrolysis. He replied, with sublime confidence: "Someday you will be collecting taxes from that theory." That kind of foresight is rare, and to expect it as standard procedure is hardly practical.

The responsibility for the development of technological advances does not depend exclusively on any one form of corporate structure. The organization of any company is, to a considerable degree, a reflection of the managerial philosophy of its chief executive; it may vary from one-man rule to a thoroughly decentralized corporation: General Electric, General Motors, and Union Carbide are all to some degree decentralized. Yet no two of them are organized exactly alike, nor does the plan of organization of any one of them persist unchanged over the years. It would be foolhardy to demand a common form of organizational structure among all companies engaged in research and development activities.

Instead, our approach should be adaptable to all kinds of organization and should also make allowances for human fallibility. In commenting on the British aircraft industry, an English publication once pointed out that the industry "has an abundance of the kind of men scarce in other industries: good planners, designers, innovators, production engineers, salesmen, a smattering of dreamers, and the occasional genius. But it is thin on the organizing men, who for all their defects translate genius into output." Finding such organizing men is what we must do in order to fix the responsibility for the development of technological advances.

METHODS OF UTILIZING TECHNOLOGY

However, part of the problem of efficient utilization is fixing the responsibility for such utilization. There are three general approaches that can help you to "translate genius into output." One we can call the "task force" method; the second, the "czar" method; and the third, the "laissez faire" method.

The most important factor in any one of the three approaches is the proper climate—an atmosphere which makes it possible for the whole organization to be drawn into the development program. Unless this exists, the effort will certainly be slower and less efficient.

Top management must assume the responsibility of seeing that the whole company is ready to accept a new development. All functions and all persons in the organization must understand that the company is interested in efficient and rapid utilization of new technology, that it welcomes change and innovation, and that it is prepared to make available the necessary tools and skills to accomplish this objective. Unless this responsibility is properly discharged, the organization will fall short of its full potential.

The task-force approach. During World War II, the Navy used the term "task force" to describe a multifunctional fighting unit composed of an aircraft carrier, destroyers, cruisers, and so forth and organized so that it could be directed toward an overall goal. The industrial task force borrowed this multifunctional concept. It is not simply another kind of committee. Too often the committee is merely a ponderous, truncated group wandering aimlessly in a jungle of divided responsibility. But the task force which is organized for a special purpose and which coordinates the various functions of a business, has had extraordinary success.

The S. C. Johnson Company, for example, has used the task-force principle to great advantage in bringing its new products to market. Very briefly, Johnson has what amounts to a permanent task force in its New Products Department; it is a top management function and reports directly to the president. This group has responsibility, in a counseling sense, for piloting an innovation from the laboratory door to the market floor. Its function is, in effect, to get the feel of market potential, to estimate probable capital investment, and to make certain that the item is one that fits into the Johnson profile of production suitability and marketing techniques.

Every potential product developed in the Johnson labs follows this route. Then, if the "fitness" tests are passed, a second task force, or sponsor group, takes over. It has the ultimate responsibility for getting the product into the hands of consumers. In addition to a member of the New Products Department, who assures continuity between the first and second task forces, the sponsor group is composed of financial and production representatives, marketing people, and—last and most important—the man who conceived the idea. This man is often put in charge of the sponsor group; if he is not, the one who has shown the greatest enthusiasm for the project may well be selected.

Johnson has found a number of advantages in using this task-force system. For one thing, the originator of the idea contributes his own enthusiasm when placed in charge of the group; for another, a total company view and almost automatic cooperation and coordination are assured, because all the functions of the business are represented. At the present time there are approximately 40 sponsor groups in operation, and the results of their efforts speak well for the task-force approach. These sponsor groups have little or no written delegation of authority, but they generally receive a budget from top management which establishes the framework within which the group may operate. Although they accomplish their results largely through persuasion, they generally do have effective authority to accomplish their ends, within budgetary limitation, because they have the full support of top management.

The czar system. Somewhat in contrast is the experience of the Corning Glass Works, the developer of "Pyroceram," which has been called "the most important technological breakthrough ever made in glass research." To capitalize on this opportunity, Corning turned to a single coordinator, or "czar."

The czar is not a new administrative concept. The Government has often employed centralized managerial responsibility to get things done; some notable examples are Bernard Baruch, the various war production coordinators, and—perhaps the best known of all—General Leslie R. Groves, whose Manhattan Project produced the atomic bomb. Today, industry is using the czar system increasingly in situations where interdivisional and interdepartmental direction and cooperation are essential. And several companies like Corning have adopted it to make certain that the product of technological research realizes its fullest potential.

Corning's "Coordinator of Pyroceram" had the complete responsibility for the ultimate marketing of its breakthrough products. He functioned as a planning, coordination, and communications center for new developments. Thus he drew on all the company's resources—research, engineering, production, finance, and marketing—to introduce the new material into the market.

Because the coordinator had this overall view of the company's potential and capabilities, Corning was able to work Pyroceram into uses ranging from defense technology to cups and saucers in the home. Since the successful introduction of Pyroceram, Corning has incorporated the coordinator concept into its organization structure by establishing the position of manager of product planning, who reports directly to the president.

The laissez-faire method. A third general approach to fixing the managerial responsibility for technological development could be called the laissez-faire method. By this we mean a system which permits each phase of the process of utilization to be carried out by the department concerned. Thus, research carries a project a certain distance, after which it is transferred to development and then to production and sales. The effective utilization of an innovation under this system depends entirely upon three factors: cooperation among the various departments, the ability of men in one department to sell those in another department on the project, and the development of personal attitudes that command respect. Corporations such as General Electric and Dow Chemical have employed this method, or a close approximation of it, to bring synthetic diamonds and fibers from the research laboratory to the marketplace.

Dow, for example, relies heavily on group liaison and open communications channels in the areas linking research, development, and sales. Research sees development as a primary customer, while development searches out applications for sales and marketing to explore more intensively. Meanwhile, manufacturing technologies and finance are brought in through the development department. Research on "Zefran," a synthetic fiber, began in 1949; it was introduced to the market in the fall of 1958. In that ten-year period, Dow had gone through the steps of tailoring an innovation to fit a particular market, creating a ten-million-dollar manufacturing facility, and marketing a radically different product —relying primarily on close-knit cooperation among individuals and departments.

Although General Electric has over 100 research facilities of one kind or another throughout the company, basic research is essentially a staff function conducted in a few central locations such as the Schenectady laboratory. In 1951 the company decided to attempt to synthesize diamonds for industrial uses. Four years later General Electric scientists announced that they had attained their goal. Finally, two and a half years later, in October 1957, General Electric's Metallurgical Products Department had a salable product.

The crucial factor in this remarkable performance was cooperation: first, between engineering and scientific research and, second, among the various divisions of the Product Department. Other departments of the company have followed the same procedures when handling a breakthrough.

General Electric, like Dow, innovates to order. For instance, a product planning group in the Specialty Motor Department draws up functional specifications for a new motor, which describe what the motor ought to *do*, not what it should *look like*. Then research, design, engineering, and manufacturing work closely together while, at an appropriate stage, the financial and marketing divisions of the business simultaneously explore the feasibility and costs of the new product. Finally, top management gives the make-or-break decision.

The combination approach. But what works for General Electric and Dow—or for Corning or Johnson—may not work for everyone. Some features of one of these three approaches to capitalizing on new products may be incompatible with organization policies. If such is the case, a company may want to use a combination approach. The American Can Company, for example, has combined the stronger features of all three methods into its own approach. Essentially, technological developments at Canco find their way to the market through an *advisory* task force— a Research Projects and Control Committee composed of general managers from the company's various functional departments; an *operating* task force—a New Products Department that rides herd on the operating departments; and a czar (in the sense that we have been using the term) —a research and development administrator.

Every Canco innovation, whether it stems from freewheeling research in the lab or is assigned initially to the lab on an invent-to-order basis, is first screened by the New Products Department for feasibility. It is then examined by the committee, where it must compete with all other proposals for approval. If the committee decides that Canco ought to invest in the idea, the New Products Department works with the research and development administrator to guide the project through manufacturing and marketing.

Both departments have an internal selling, persuading, and managing job to do; both can call on the committee for help; and both are represented on the committee. Finally, to make certain that projects undertaken in Canco research centers are within the general province of the company's interests, the committee passes on the bulk of the projects assigned for scientific investigation.

PREREQUISITES FOR SUCCESS

What makes these four approaches successful? Top management cannot appoint a task force, for example, and simply say, "Go ahead: turn this innovation into a salable product." Specific criteria and guidelines must be laid down, objectives must be established, responsibility fixed, and authority delegated.

Every project must meet certain criteria:

• What are the company's capabilities in the area into which we intend to move?
• What are the advantages and disadvantages?
• Do we have a physical plant capable of producing the product, or can we engineer and build one?
• What is our financial position?

- Does our management experience fit us for the task?
- Do we have the personnel required?
- Do we have the special skills needed?
- What are the real reasons for the success or failure of our past projects?

There are many other criteria, but if the project survives an analysis of this sort, we are ready to go.

The purpose of having a set of objectives is twofold: to provide a goal and to measure performance. Objectives vary with the level of management and the particular stage in the development of a breakthrough. These objectives should be set by those responsible for the project with the help, counsel, and approval of top management, and they should be presented in full and in writing as a product plan.

We must determine which men are to be responsible and how they will be chosen. Any one of the various methods we have considered can work, provided the leadership is adequate. It is imperative, in any case, to have a man or group of men with enthusiasm for the project, confidence in their own ability, and the qualities of persuasion and leadership which can create the desire in others to cooperate and perform above and beyond the call of duty. These qualities are equal in importance to the specific skills and knowledge of engineering, markets, and other business functions, but neither group of qualifications can be successful without the other.

There must also be a clear delegation of authority and responsibility. This, after all, is the essence of effective decision making. Whether a company names an individual or a group to supervise a technological innovation from its discovery in research to its final destination in the marketplace or whether teamwork is used to get the job done, the success of the undertaking will hinge largely on the quality of decision making involved. This means pushing the decision-making process down to the organization level where it is applicable. Clearly defining areas of responsibility creates an atmosphere of freedom in which the individual can work productively.

My company fosters this idea to the best of its ability. We try to provide freedom to innovate, to create, to take calculated risks, and to do what needs to be done to achieve a predetermined objective. In this process, the supervisor-subordinate relationship undergoes a subtle revision: the supervisor assists the subordinate to get his job done, and top management, in effect, becomes available on a cooperative basis to those who are charged with operating responsibility. If a manager is successful in creating a productive climate, he will have discharged a major responsibility for the effective utilization of new technology.

Furthermore, regardless of the system chosen in a given instance, he will stand a better chance of success.

* * *

In today's accelerating economy, we can no longer afford to let nature take its course in the utilization of new technology. We must speed up the process again and again to remain competitive. Indeed, the problems of economic and national survival leave no alternative. We must devote more time and effort to solving the problems which still prevent us from making the journey from the idea to the practical application at rocket speed instead of at a horse-and-buggy pace.

STAFFING AND COMPENSATION

THE GROWING JOB OF
TECHNICAL RECRUITING •

ARNOLD R. DEUTSCH

IN A PERIOD OF COMPETITIVE innovation stemming from an almost stagger-
ing profusion of technical advances, many company managements are side-
stepping one of their major corporate functions by delegating well down
in the organization an operation that directly affects the success or failure
of their firms. That function is the recruiting of engineers and scientists.

Though the search for technical talent has been on for more than 12
years, technical manpower recruiting continues to be regarded as a minor
activity in many companies. Its long-range importance is seldom appreciated; it is, in fact, seldom considered as anything more than a necessary
but routine task.

This is due in part to its origin. Initiated as an emergency measure to
meet what was seen as a transient need, recruiting has never outgrown its
own beginnings in the eyes of management. As a result, after more than a
decade of intense recruiting activity, and with the prospect of at least
another such decade ahead, most management people still tend to consider
this a temporary function.

Nor is recruiting an isolated activity, though it is frequently so regarded.
It is, in fact, closely interrelated with all factors affecting technical people
within the company, with their productivity, and with the costly problems
of technical turnover.

Another fact too seldom considered is this: recruiting has to do not only
with the quantity of technical people the company may require but with
the quality of people it can attract. As R. E. Lewis, president of Perkin-
Elmer Corporation, has pointed out, "From now on, the growth and success

---

ARNOLD R. DEUTSCH is President, Deutsch & Shea, Inc., New York, New York.

of your company will be determined by the creation of new concepts in products—not by the rehashing of old products, steadily but slowly improved. Because only engineers and scientists can bring forth this steady stream of new product concepts and techniques, it is these scientists and engineers who hold in their hands the key to any company's success."[1]

It follows that the firm that must settle for second or third best in either the quantity or, especially, the quality of technical talent it can muster will inevitably fall behind the competitor who has been able to assemble a first-rank team of engineers and scientists, retain them, and stimulate them to high creative effort. Further, it will find itself in the vicious cycle of being unable to attract or retain top-rank technical minds, because the level of technical achievement and the level of its professional personnel will not offer sufficient inducement to such men. Given these parameters, recruiting is not a minor function, but a key element in corporate survival.

Technical recruiting today does receive some encouragement and support from top management, as technical recruiting executives themselves acknowledge. But it is primarily encouragement to meet current needs rather than to develop long-range programs. It is the support of present outmoded methods and not the development of new and more effective recruiting techniques. What is needed is top executive awareness of technical recruiting as a long-range, broad-scale venture, real insight into current recruiting methods, and a new and wider concept of how recruiting could be handled and the benefits that it could provide a forward-looking firm.

THE NECESSITY FOR RECRUITING

Engineers and scientists are not off-the-shelf items to be requisitioned as needed. The necessity for recruiting stems from the fact that in many fields there are not enough trained professionals to go around. Nor are there likely to be enough engineers and scientists to meet the demands of the immediate future.

Like the sorcerer's apprentice, we see the technology we have created multiplying itself with increasing rapidity. Each step forward in engineering, each success in science creates a need for more technical people to explore and exploit the breakthrough. "The need for engineers in a greater number of specialties is the inevitable result of the twentieth century's crescendo of invention and industrial change," Hilliard W. Paige, general manager of General Electric's Missile and Space Vehicle Department, has said. He

---

[1] Remarks before the International Convention of the Institute of Radio Engineers, March 21, 1961.

added that "the need for engineers is not only curving upward today—it is curving upward *exponentially*."[2]

And technological advances have made the requirements for specialized manpower more stringent. In the early days of technical recruiting, recruiters joked that if the body was warm and had an engineering degree, they'd hire it. Today's typical job specification often calls for a man with five to ten years' experience in an exotic technical field that did not exist a dozen years ago.

It is misleading to speak of an "engineering shortage," both because the term itself is so broad and also because other groups—physicists, mathematicians, chemists—are sought by industry today. More accurately, then, one might say that there are not enough engineers and scientists to supply the demand for particular areas of specific industries, such as electronics, aerospace, nucleonics, and chemicals. And it must be remembered that "engineers" and "scientists" are not identical pieces that, like those in a machine, are interchangeable. A civil engineer, for example, could not design a memory core for a digital computer, nor could an electronics engineer plan a hardened silo for an ICBM—though both are "engineers." Even within the same discipline there is little interchangeability: a man who designs massive dynamos cannot switch jobs with a researcher in microelectronics, though both may have the same electrical engineering degree from the same school.

The continually growing need for specialists that has been caused by technical advances and the increased complexity of today's products, coupled with the inadequate supply of such engineers and scientists in many fields, has resulted in the intense competition we now face for available technical manpower. It is this need, this lack, and this competition that make technical manpower recruiting a necessity for any company that must maintain a staff of scientists and engineers.

RECRUITING SINCE 1950

When this intense demand for engineers first developed in 1950, company personnel turned to the same techniques that had been used during World War II to recruit shop help, ship builders, and secretaries: the classified pages of the local newspaper. Because local areas could not always supply the professional men needed, this advertising was extended: first to classified pages in other cities and then to the pages of technical journals. The field trip followed: a team of recruiters traveling to various cities and interviewing the technical men who responded to advertising placed in

2 Remarks before the Franklin Institute, February 24, 1960.

advance of their arrival. At one point it was not uncommon for companies to cover regularly a hundred or more cities in this manner.

Technical conventions and conferences, concentrating hundreds and sometimes thousands of engineers and scientists in a single city, offered recruiting advantages that were quickly exploited. A standard procedure was the hospitality suite with its refreshments, liquid and otherwise. These suites were widely advertised as a means of attracting engineers and scientists within reach of the recruiter's pitch, and the conventions themselves began to assume something of a carnival tone, with stunts and gimmicks to attract the attention of the assembled technical people. When some societies attempted to restore dignity by banning recruiting at their meetings, recruiters and the middlemen who had now entered the picture simply set up shop outside a society's jurisdiction.

In the beginning, overselling was the rule in recruiting, and the pictures painted by recruiter-salesmen had little relation to industrial reality. In consequence, turnover among technical people was high, as newly hired men found the expected benefits in work assignments, advancement, facilities, and recognition did not materialize. This turnover rate was swelled by discontented technical staff members who heard, second hand, of their company's offers to prospects of advantages and benefits that they themselves did not enjoy.

College recruiting, too, became a semiannual phenomenon; on some campuses reportedly more recruiters were on hand than graduating technical students. Some of these recruiters proved more adept at selling students on the company than presenting a realistic view of what the new engineer would find on the job, but their stories were backed up by the ever higher starting salaries they offered.

This resulted almost immediately in adverse effects. The turnover rate among these new engineers became exceedingly high. Although wooed by visions of glamorous assignments, they found themselves handling routine and sometimes subprofessional jobs; their high starting salaries often precluded further salary advances for long periods. And these same starting rates provoked great discontent among the more experienced technical men, who saw the differential between their own salaries and those of inexperienced newcomers rapidly diminishing.

Recruiting by mail was used with some regularity, and technical men in interviews with our research staff reported receiving as many as a dozen recruiting letters a week. A few firms supplemented their letters with high-fidelity recordings of their "recruiting pitch." Even recruiting by telephone was practiced, generally by one of the middleman organizations. Such solicitation did not stop with calling the technical man at his home; many technical people reported receiving such telephone calls at work.

One effective technique developed during this period was the internal referral program. Staff engineers and scientists, encouraged by their supervisors, contacted colleagues and brought to their attention the openings and advantages of the company. Because it was feasible only among groups with high morale and utilized word-of-mouth recommendation, a type of communication technical people find highly acceptable, the internal referral program was, and continues to be, quite successful in recruiting men of above-average quality at minimum cost.

Throughout the past 12 years, however, the mainstay of the recruiting efforts of most firms has been advertising. A few companies have tried general magazines, radio, and television, but these experiments have been short-lived. The bulk of recruitment advertising was and is placed in newspapers and technical journals and plays the major role in securing for a company the engineers and the scientists it must have.

CURRENT PROBLEMS IN RECRUITING

There are some problems at the operational level in recruiting which persist from year to year. One which is much criticized by technical people is the slowness with which the majority of firms process applications that result from their expensive recruiting efforts. The solution to this is often outside the hands of recruiting people, who must wait upon decisions from technical supervisors and administrators. One director of technical recruiting calls such delays the major cause of recruiting failure and wasted dollars, because with many opportunities to choose from, engineers and scientists are not content to wait weeks for an answer to their applications.

Other complaints center around lack of replies by companies to résumés or letters sent in response to recruiting ads. The technical man usually concludes the company is not really interested in hiring and passes this comment on to his colleagues. Unprofessional facilities at interviews, poor impressions made at these interviews (including being kept waiting for long periods), unnecessary and cumbersome application forms, and similar matters are other causes for complaint. Although these may seem to be minor points, they cause companies to lose the services of good men and waste the cost of securing their applications. Such tactics also adversely affect the company's reputation as an employer of technical men.

A more important problem centers on the recruiting techniques used today. Though somewhat refined and improved, these are still the methods adopted to meet the old emergency situation—the résumé, ads, field trips, convention recruiting, and so on. Some of the other, secondary techniques have reached a literal point of no return; some are becoming bad public relations for the company using them.

Convention recruiting, for instance, through some of its excesses, is building a poor image of both professional societies and companies. For this reason, and because such recruiting interferes in some instances with the transmission of technical information, it is coming under fire from the technical community. Similar campus recruiting practices have resulted in the formation by most universities of a code of ethics to which companies must agree to adhere in their campus recruiting efforts.

The hard-sell style that marked much of earlier recruitment advertising has given way to more refined approaches matching the experience and sophistication of a technical audience that has been barraged with recruitment material for a dozen years. Many companies, however, continue to depend on advertising alone to do the recruiting job which the firm is obviously not capable of doing by itself.

Recruiting today is in a kind of stalemate: each company is using the methods, claims, and approaches of all the others engaged in the search for technical manpower. And there is little in all of this that accords with the basic interests and psychology of technical people.

The most basic problem, perhaps, stems from management itself: the generally held management view that technical manpower recruiting is a short-range activity of limited value. This attitude is reflected most clearly by some companies in which recruiting is seen as a purely temporary activity—halted when current needs are filled, revived when another batch of engineers and scientists is needed.

Even to the men who direct and take part in it, the recruiting function is seen as a limited one. Two-thirds of a group of 40 directors of technical recruiting who took part in a survey saw their job as a stepping stone to another position rather than a career in itself.[3] Most of these men had under five years' experience in their positions, and the majority of the recruiters they employed had three years or less. As one director noted, "In my opinion, a major problem which produces high recruiting costs can be traced to poor selection of recruiting talent and the tendency to use recruiting offices as training grounds for junior personnel trainees."

It would seem that top executives, with wide responsibilities for the long-range planning of their companies, too often neglect the future input of technical talent that will in a very real sense affect all other aspects of corporate planning. What can management do? First, it can acquire as thorough an understanding as possible of the motivations and drives of the technical people whose role in industry becomes increasingly important. Second, it can press for the development of improved methods for predicting the company's technical manpower needs. Third, it can review present

[3] *Industrial Relations News*, May 27, 1961.

approaches to technical manpower recruiting with a view toward improving techniques and raising its status as a corporate function.

UNDERSTANDING ENGINEERS AND SCIENTISTS

As far back as 1952, Peter Drucker pointed out some of the differences in basic attitudes between management and technical people.[4] These differences are still little recognized. Assuming and acting on the assumption that engineers and scientists are, in their drives and motivations, basically similar to management people is to compound a widespread error that accounts for much of the discontent among professional people in industry. As Frederick J. Harbison, director of Princeton University's Industrial Relations Section, noted:

> American industry has only begun to comprehend its managerial problems in this area. The scientist tends to resist industry's concept of "executive authority" and he does not readily accept the goals of the corporation. He has his own goals, which are scientific in nature, and he has been brought up to respect the authority of his scientific colleagues rather than the authority of corporate managers. . . . And above all [industry] needs to discard the notion that scientists are like any other group of employees, because the well-tried principles of good personnel administration simply won't work with today's modern eggheads.[5]

Insofar as recruiting technical people is concerned, there are two major factors in the make-up of these professionals that management should recognize:

1. The primary motivating factor in job selection by technical people is the nature of the work itself. The interest, the challenge to their technical abilities, and the opportunities for significant professional achievement offered by the work to be done determine whether or not an engineer or scientist will consider a position. Study after study has confirmed this.
2. Second only to the nature of the work as a motivating factor is the technical man's perception of the company as a place for professional work. He searches for optimum freedom in handling assignments and responsibility for his work. He wants recognition for his contributions within the company, opportunities to gain recognition in the outside technical community, and the status and prerogatives due him as a professional.

This is not to say that such material factors as salary and location do not

[4] "Management and the Professional Employee," *Harvard Business Review,* May-June, 1952.
[5] "More Chiefs, Fewer Indians," *University,* Winter, 1961.

play a role in job choice, because they do. But in themselves neither is sufficient to attract the professional; their principal value in recruiting is to tip the scales among equally appealing opportunities.

EMPLOYER IMAGE

The concept of employer image is basic to any discussion of the motivations of technical people. The ideas of "brand image" for a consumer product and "corporate image" for a firm are widely accepted. A company which employs engineers and scientists has an "employer image" as well. This is its reputation in the technical community as a potential employer. Studies indicate that this employer image is remarkably consistent among technical people; it crosses the boundaries of technical disciplines and persists over long periods. The importance of employer image to the company has been succinctly described by Dr. Saul Gellerman, psychologist and management consultant:

> . . . companies that are prospective employers are being subjected to a constant, unorganized but highly selective screening process that largely determines which of these men will apply to a given company at all . . . This is the point where the good ones get away and at which the leftovers tend to gravitate toward certain luckless firms.[6]

A favorable image among engineers and scientists is based principally on a perception of the company as progressive in its technological achievements and as recognizing the importance and professional status of its technical staff. Employer image develops early: college seniors in the technical disciplines already have definite concepts about companies as potential employers; graduate students have employer images even more detailed.

The primary image source among both students and experienced technical men is the same, and it is also the source on which engineers and scientists tend to rely most heavily for current technical information: personal contacts with colleagues. The most effective contacts in creating employer images are with actual employees or representatives of the company, but second- and third-hand reports that circulate within the technical community form the basis for most employer images.

PROFESSIONAL CLIMATE

Effective technical recruiting, then, begins with the company's own engineers and scientists. Their attitudes, expressed in informal conversations

---

[6] Gellerman, Saul W., "The Company Employment Image," MANAGEMENT REVIEW, March 1960.

with professional colleagues, are the key to employer image, which in turn affects not only the success of the company's recruiting efforts but the quality of technical men who respond to them.

Fostering high morale among company engineers and scientists is the basic step both for recruiting and for achieving higher technical productivity and lower turnover among technical people. The elements which make up an atmosphere conducive to high professional morale have been cited before. But there are five key points in creating an optimum climate for professional people that should be stressed:

1. *Effective communications* not only upward to and downward from management but laterally among the various technical departments. Only good communications can overcome the barriers that different goals and motivations have raised between management and technical people.

2. *Recognition* is the most sought after reward among technical people in industry. They need company recognition of their contributions and of their status as professionals and recognition of their professional achievements by their colleagues outside. This is perhaps the single most important facet of good professional climate.

3. *Optimum salary and benefits* based on individual contributions rather than mass formulas are sought by technical people. A particular problem area is the feeling that their own salaries and benefits are not comparable to those of equivalent management positions.

4. *Freedom and responsibility* are important to the professional man because they are ingredients of being professional. The right to deal with a technical problem in a way he himself chooses or the larger freedom of the researcher to choose areas of investigation is one side of the professional coin, the reverse of which is the need to make decisions, to get the job done, to handle a total job rather than a segment. Management policies frequently frustrate these desires because there is a lack of understanding of the nature of engineering and science.

5. *Optimum utilization* of the technical person is a goal he himself seeks. He wants to work at a professional level and not do technician's work; he wants to devote himself to his specialization with a minimum of routine and paperwork; he wants to do a solid, thorough job rather than a makeshift one. He feels better coordination in the company is needed if he is to achieve this goal.

When a company has a favorable climate for technical people, they themselves will be the principal tool in attracting other professional people to the company.

It is the search for a climate containing the factors listed above that motivates much of the turnover among technical people today. It is the absence of such a climate that has led many talented technical people to leave their firms either to work elsewhere or to set up their own companies.

PREDICTING MANPOWER NEEDS

How many technical people will a company need 10 years from now and in what specialties? It is likely that an answer to these questions has never been seriously sought in many companies. Yet the ability to predict within reasonable limits the numbers and kinds of technical people required would enable recruiting to be planned and budgeted over an extended period and would eliminate the waste of stop-start and crash programs. It would also enable the company to train its own specialists in fields where a tight supply of professional manpower could be expected.

Such planning must march in step with long-range company goals and would serve to place manpower acquisition on the same basis as the development of facilities and funding. The resulting awareness, among all echelons of management, of technical talent as a tangible and important company asset would assist in establishing and maintaining a climate favorable to professional people.

The momentum of technological advance makes such prediction difficult, but it may also provide the necessary tools. Perhaps they are already at hand in the digital computer, operations research and games theory, and in advanced mathematics. What is needed here, as elsewhere in the recruiting process, is management pressure for solutions.

NEW DIRECTIONS IN RECRUITING

Recruiting is in many ways a communications function. The company must communicate its openings and advantages; the prospect, his interest and qualifications. But the communications channels in recruiting are often jammed because of the increasing number of firms using them and the similarity of the messages transmitted. A look at the business section of a Sunday *New York Times* reveals what an acoustics engineer might call "a high ambient noise level." So many voices are demanding attention that few single voices really get through. Thus it is with most recruiting efforts today.

What is called for is a company program whose basic function is to communicate regularly to the technical community the material which most closely affects the attitudes of engineers and scientists toward companies as employers; and this material should be transmitted primarily through channels technical people themselves find most acceptable. The activities of some progressive companies provide examples of the new directions in which technical manpower recruiting could move.

In 1957, General Electric's Missiles and Space Vehicles Department moved to Philadelphia, where expansion required hiring a large number of technical people. To meet this need MSVD developed a technical symposium on current advances in space flight. The speakers were of top rank, nationally known scientists of the department; the material presented covered new technical achievements by the organization of great interest to professionals in this field. In addition to the four speakers, a number of other technical people from the department were on hand, and ample opportunity for informal discussion was provided.

The symposium, held originally in Philadelphia, was repeated in New York, Boston, and Washington. Several hundred engineers and scientists, their professional qualifications screened in advance, attended each session. The interest generated by these meetings brought the newly formed organization to the attention of an even wider technical audience. The end result was enough interested inquiries and contacts from technical people to aid materially in staffing the new operation.

This illustrates an approach to recruiting that might be called *the technical event:* the use of seminars, symposiums, exhibits, and similar meetings devoted to providing worthwhile and interesting information and experience to a select group of engineers and scientists. This approach has the double virtue of enabling the company to put its best technical foot forward, of demonstrating in factual terms its technical achievements, and at the same time of providing a worthwhile reward to the technical people who attend. Holding such events on a regular basis would keep the company in constant and favorable contact with the technical community, with resulting benefits in recruiting.

The Kearfott Division of General Precision Aerospace, a medium-sized New Jersey company manufacturing precision equipment, recently provided an interesting example of another possible approach to recruiting. The company bought Sunday afternoon time on a well-known television station whose coverage included most of the northern New Jersey and New York City metropolitan areas. In this time they ran a film that had been prepared to acquaint employees with the company's technical achievements. (The problem of communicating with employees working in different plants and shifts led to the decision to use television rather than to show the film to individual groups.) Following the film there was a discussion in which one of the company's leading scientists played an important role. The program was well advertised in advance, not only among employees but also in the communities the program covered. In this way it served a triple purpose: internal communication to all employees, general community relations, and a demonstration to the local technical community of the achievements of the company and of the esteem in which it held its professional people.

Though this program was not intended as a recruiting device, it suggests another worthwhile approach to the problem: the development of community relations programs directed toward the technical people in areas adjacent to the company's location. The objective of such programs would be to familiarize local engineers and scientists with the company's technical achievements and to provide the opportunities for personal contact which prove so effective in creating good employer image. Among methods that might be used are holding open house for technical people at company plants and laboratories, participation by company personnel in local technical groups and societies, encouragement of company engineers and scientists to act as speakers, teachers, advisers, and aides in other community activities.

In a sense, both of the foregoing examples are technical public relations. Each paper presented by a company's engineering staff, each article by a company scientist published in a technical journal, is also a form of technical public relations. For there is a technical public different from the buying public, the voting public, and similar groups. Its existence, however, is seldom recognized.

Conventional public relations techniques are of little value in reaching this group. By training and attitude, engineers and scientists are fact-oriented and analytical. Attempts to use emotional appeals or slanted presentations in a professional context are likely to boomerang. The presentation of worthwhile material relating to their professional interests, however, is effective in creating a favorable image of the company.

An excellent example of technical public relations is the publication of technical journals by such companies as IBM and Bell Laboratories. These are comparable in content and format to the best professional society or commercial journals. They are widely distributed and because of the value of their content, widely read. Each issue demonstrates afresh to the technical community both the technical competence of the company that prepares it and the importance of the technical man to that company.

Another example is an advertising campaign conducted by the Esso Research and Engineering Company which serves a technical public relations function. Rather than selling, it discusses, in highly technical language, current basic scientific work under way in laboratories, with the admitted objective not only of communicating more effectively with the technical community but of serving a recruiting function as well.

These and other aspects of technical public relations represent a fresh approach to technical recruiting: a program directed at developing a favorable employer image for the company and generating a steady stream of applicants for technical positions at the company.

AN INTEGRATED PROGRAM

It should be noted that the examples cited here are isolated ones, and the methods suggested are not in themselves new. What is new is the recommendation that these techniques be integrated into a continuing program aimed at filling immediate manpower needs and providing over a period of time an employer image attractive to the high caliber technical people who can best strengthen the company's competitive position in the years to come. Such a program has precedent in the adoption of public relations activities by industry, now an almost universal fixture.

The essence of the philosophy outlined here is that a company—by designing its recruiting activities to the psychological measure of technical people—can reverse the current situation and find itself in the enviable position of being sought out by reputable engineers and scientists in its field. To develop such a program requires a number of changes, many of which center on management's own attitudes.

MANAGEMENT'S ROLE IN RECRUITING

To be a successful recruiter of technical people requires first that a company be a successful *employer* of them. The creation of a favorable climate for professional people is of basic importance in this regard. Management's role is the removal of those elements already present that cause engineers and scientists to leave the company and to institute such practices and policies as will provide the best professional climate.

As a next step, a re-examination by management of its own attitudes toward recruiting may be in order. The feeling that this is a temporary function and one that is not quite legitimate or worthwhile is not uncommon in business today. This short-range, negative view accounts for the low status of recruiting activity in many companies.

Management must arrive at its own long-range evaluation of recruiting and base it on an understanding of the long-term impact upon and values for the company implicit in this activity. It must recognize the need for continuity of recruiting effort irrespective of the short-term fluctuations in the need for manpower. And having acquired these insights, management must impress upon those directly responsible for recruiting its own positive attitudes toward this function.

Improved prediction of the company's manpower needs has already been mentioned as an essential step that needs the support of management to be achieved. Management should also take into consideration the basic problem in all recruiting: the national lack of technically trained manpower in many fields. The present limited supply of technical people graduated from our universities can have dangerous effects upon the whole economic structure if not checked. It will be to the individual firm's own benefit to inquire into means for improving this situation.

If such an approach to recruiting is to be adopted, recruiting must necessarily encompass areas beyond its present limits. This suggests that the technical personnel function or the industrial relations function will have to be raised in corporate status. Indeed, considering the growing importance and number of technical people within most companies and their profound effect on future growth and profitability, it is not unlikely that many companies will create high-level executive positions to deal with all of the facets of company-professional relationships. This would involve not only recruiting but also company communications with its technical staff, recognition for them both internally and externally, facilities planning, training and education, company relations with the technical community, and all other elements affecting the morale and utilization of engineers and scientists.

This is an ambitious undertaking, but its value to the company goes far beyond the acquisition of top technical men. Most of the methods suggested provide opportunities for the company to give technical people the recognition that stimulates them to additional achievement. Using these methods should materially reduce the high turnover rate among professionals and cut the sizable costs entailed in replacement, in training, and in the disruption of important company projects.

There is another major advantage: to base recruitment activities on the concept of the communication of technical information to the national community of engineers and scientists is also to reach the technical men who are increasingly making or shaping the decisions on buying and contract awards in industry.

Because the tempo of recruiting effort is now accelerating, this is a good time for management to undertake a broad review of the recruiting function. It is one of the most valuable and productive of a company's activities, and it deserves more attention than it has yet been granted in most companies.

THE SELECTION OF RESEARCHERS •

WILBUR C. MYERS

O RGANIZED RESEARCH OUTSIDE THE academic environment is a relatively modern development; yet its rapid expansion and acceptance in recent years has already resulted in a shortage of qualified researchers. With the enormous growth in scientific knowledge, the problem has been further aggravated by the increasing complexity of technology and the requirement for interdisciplinary research teams. Virtually every modern research laboratory is faced today with the need to enlarge its scope of activities in at least one or more new directions. In many cases this will mean the acquisition of new research personnel.

One solution that the research director has to the problems just cited is *quality* in his staff. Selecting researchers on the basis of quality is the key to the future strength and ultimate potential of the research organization. Often, however, there is a lack of appreciation on the part of the laboratory and its representatives for the hazards and subtleties involved in selecting new personnel, principally because of their involvement with the assessment of people. Consider, too, that the applicant also has a very real stake in the selection process, since in many cases his entire professional future may be involved. Therefore, as knowledge and awareness of the human factors in the selection process become more widespread, both industry and the research applicant will benefit.

The techniques for selecting researchers to be discussed are based upon the following thesis: evaluation is a two-way affair. In other words, while the research applicant is being appraised by management, he should

WILBUR C. MYERS is Director of Research, Electronics Division, The National Cash Register Company, Hawthorne, California.

be given ample opportunity to evaluate the research position for which he is being considered.

LOCATING THE APPLICANT

It is no secret that well-qualified scientists and engineers capable of conducting productive research programs are both difficult and expensive to locate. For a recruiting program to be successful, planning is essential. A variety of recruiting techniques are available once the particular approach has been selected, depending upon the types of technical skills and scientific disciplines required. Adequate lead time must also be provided when planning a recruiting program.

Another requirement for planning a successful recruiting program is the advance consideration of its effect upon the present staff. Their active cooperation will be an important factor since, in all probability, they will be called upon to play various roles during the selection process. Ultimately, the staff will assist in integrating the new personnel into the research organization, an operation demanding care and finesse.

Locating researchers can be broadly classified into the areas of college recruiting and the recruiting of experienced personnel. W. W. Wagner has an excellent discussion of the methods and problems in each area.[1] He also discusses the use of supplementary programs such as student cooperative training programs for undergraduates as well as management development programs for upgrading existing employees.

In addition to the need for scientists and engineers, the research organization must be provided with various kinds of nonprofessional skills and services. Such services are usually obtained by the addition of technicians and technical assistants to the professional staff of the laboratory. Although almost all research laboratories employ such personnel, there exists little in the way of general agreement upon the following:

1. What is the need for nonprofessional personnel in research?
2. Can an increase in nonprofessionals help to alleviate the shortage of scientists now and in the years ahead?
3. What is the optimum ratio of professionals to nonprofessionals?
4. What kinds of work should be assigned to technicians?
5. How should technicians be trained and educated?
6. How and where can technicians be located and hired?

These were some of the questions that prompted the American Institute of Physics to hold a conference on the recruitment and training of tech-

---

[1] "Methods of Recruiting Engineers," in *Optimum Use of Engineering Talent*, Management Report 58, American Management Association, New York, 1961.

nicians in physics. Participants of the conference answered the first two questions in the affirmative, and although no panacea was found, they provided information, advice, and encouragement to the AIP staff in seeking answers to the remaining questions.[2]

Important to the success of most forms of recruiting is attractive and effective advertising. Since advertising is both expensive and quite unpredictable, it follows that considerable care should be applied to its use. It will normally be a wise investment to employ an advertising agency to work with the personnel and the research departments in planning the advertising campaign. Careful study should be given to the copy, artwork, and layout used in the ads as well as to the media used for placement. "Blind" ads are normally used only on rare occasions where special circumstances warrant. *Acknowledgment should be made to all inquiries received from recruiting advertisements.* Unfortunately, the common practice is to answer only those inquiries where further follow-up is desired. Such practices contribute to poor public relations and dilute any goodwill the advertising may create.

All but the most modest recruiting programs represent the expenditure of much time, money, and effort. Applicants no longer wait in line to be hired. Furthermore, a really well-qualified research applicant today more often than not has a choice of openings. Thus, most organizations find themselves in a most competitive situation. It would appear—upon economic reasons alone—that once an applicant had been located for evaluation, a well-organized plan should be used to review his qualifications.[3]

MANAGEMENT'S EVALUATION OF THE RESEARCH APPLICANT

Management's evaluation of the research applicant can be divided into two general categories: (1) information on the applicant's qualifications and background and (2) factors which can be used to appraise the applicant's suitability for the specific research assignment involved.

Information on the research applicant's qualifications and background is ordinarily obtained through the use of one or more relatively standard methods. The thoroughness with which this information needs to be developed will depend to a large extent upon the nature of the position which must be filled. The following methods are commonly used:

[2] "Technical Assistants in Physics in the United States," *Physics Today,* March 1963.

[3] See Cooper, H. B. H., and Wing, Harold F. "Selecting the Engineering Applicant," in *Optimum Use of Engineering Talent,* Management Report 58, American Management Association, New York, 1961 and Speroff, B. J., "Selecting and Inducting Employees," *Personnel Journal,* December 1959.

1. *Standard employment application form.* For practical reasons such a form should be as concise and simple as possible.
2. *Résumé prepared by the applicant.* The manner in which the résumé is written often reveals a great deal about an applicant's qualifications which is not shown by the actual contents of the résumé.
3. *References.* There are three types of references: personal and character references, professional references, and previous-employer references. With respect to previous employers, the most success is usually obtained by first telephoning the applicant's former supervisor and then following up with a routine form letter to be filled out for the personnel record. This technique often elicits candid comments which would never appear in writing. Also, many form letters are processed on a routine basis by personnel department employees who have only a very limited actual knowledge of the applicant's qualifications and work history. Contacts with an applicant's present employer should, of course, be made only with his approval.
4. *Academic transcripts.* Records of this type are of value only for recent graduates. Experienced applicants should be judged primarily by what they have been able to accomplish once out of college rather than by their scholastic grades.
5. *Personal interviews.* Several forms of interviews are employed in the evaluation and selection process, and much has been written on the subject.[4] After a preliminary or screening interview with the applicant, it is very important wherever possible to conduct any further interviews at the employment location. The applicant and his potential supervisor and associates should have the opportunity to meet each other there, preferably in the relaxed atmosphere of a luncheon. However, when definite appointments have been scheduled in advance with an applicant, it is only common courtesy to honor them. If the applicant arrives for his interview on time and is kept waiting unnecessarily, the whole interview starts off on a bad note. Also, the applicant may have another appointment scheduled later, and delays of this kind will cut short the time available for the first interview.
6. *Testing.* The use of various forms of testing programs are becoming more and more common. Although testing is a controversial subject,

[4] See Balinsky, B., and Burger, R., "The Selection Interview," in *The Executive Interview,* Harper & Brothers, New York, 1959 and Fear, R. A., *The Evaluation Interview,* McGraw-Hill Book Company, New York, 1958.

most users believe the tests to be beneficial if properly applied. Users further emphasize that the tests merely supplement, not replace, such necessary tools as the interview and the application form. As a word of caution, testing is not a field for amateurs, and a professionally administered program is a must. When a key supervisory position has to be filled, it is often valuable to employ the services of a reputable management consulting firm that specializes in executive testing and evaluation.

The factors used for evaluation of an applicant can be divided into two categories: technical qualifications and personal characteristics. Both of these areas must be balanced with respect to each other in order to obtain an individual who will integrate well into an existing organization. Too often in research an applicant is hired on the basis of a brilliant academic record, and only later is it discovered that he cannot work well with his associates or his supervisor.

Technical qualifications include (1) academic background and record, (2) special training, (3) honors and awards, (4) publications and patents, and (5) professional affiliations. Other technical qualifications which are more difficult to evaluate initially are organizational and planning ability, analytical skill, mechanical aptitude, effectiveness in communication, and creativity and originality.

Because of its obvious importance to research, the subject of creativity and originality in an applicant deserves special attention. Individuals with creative ability are rare, and yet the very success of any laboratory vitally depends upon the securing of researchers from this select group. Although much confusion seems to exist on the subject and there are no definitive means to determine in advance whether an applicant has this ability, much can be learned by carefully reviewing the literature on the subject.[5]

Personal characteristics include (1) professional integrity, (2) general character—especially honesty—(3) initiative and enthusiasm, (4) judgment, (5) adaptability to change, (6) leadership potential, (7) responsibility and maturity, (8) cooperation with and attitude toward associates, (9) dependability and capacity to follow through on a job, (10) temperament—especially tact—(11) personal appearance, and (12) health. At some time during the course of the interview, it should be clearly established

5 See Jones, S. L., and Arnold, J. E., "The Creative Individual in Industrial Research," *IRE Transactions on Engineering Management,* June 1962; MacKinnon, D. W., "What Makes A Person Creative?" *Saturday Review,* February 10, 1962; Hurt, R., "Personality Traits of Creative Research and Development Personnel," *Research/Development,* September 1961; Walkup, L. E., "Individual Creativity," *Industrial Laboratories,* November 1958; and Kelley, M. J., "Understanding the Creative Process," *Chemical and Engineering News,* March 25, 1957.

why the applicant is considering a change from his present employment. This is particularly important in the case of a research applicant because of the relatively long time it takes to integrate a new man into a research program. Factors which might lead to early turnover or initial misassignment must be consciously investigated during the interview.

A serious attempt should also be made to determine the motives and future goals of the applicant. Discussion of the type of research assignments and problems he liked best in the past is often helpful here; likewise, discussion of those assignments he liked least may also prove enlightening to the interviewer.

THE APPLICANT'S EVALUATION OF THE POSITION

The research applicant's evaluation of the position to be filled can be divided broadly into two parts: general information about the company and its research programs and a review of the growth potential available to the applicant.

There are a number of different ways of providing general information about the company and its research programs to the research applicant. The following approaches are available to most research organizations.

Company Literature. Various items may be given to the research applicant for review either prior to his interview or afterward. Some typical examples of this material are:

- A printed brochure describing the company's fields of scientific research, research facilities, organization structure, and research policies.

- The annual financial report of the company.

- Selected reprints of published work originating from research programs conducted at the company's laboratory.

- Printed brochures describing personnel policies and benefit plans.

Properly handled, such materials can very effectively serve as "silent salesmen" and if made available in advance of the formal interview, save the interviewer a fair amount of time.

A guided tour of research facilities. This tour should include not only the laboratory itself but also the service facilities, such as the library, model shop, and instrument room. In far too many cases, the research applicant never has an opportunity to see anything beyond the lobby and the personnel department of the company that is interviewing him. Presumably, most organizations are proud of their laboratories and facilities; they should therefore welcome such a guided tour as an additional means of selling the research applicant.

Personal contact with research staff members and the applicant's potential supervisor. After the formalities of the interview and preliminary screening process are over, adequate time should be provided for the applicant to talk to laboratory staff members and to his prospective supervisor. If possible, he should also have the opportunity to meet his prospective department head. This personal contact gives the applicant a chance to appraise the type of individuals he would be associated with if he joined the company. It also gives him an opportunity to ask further questions about the organization and the kind of work it is engaged in. This is a most important phase of the two-way approach to the evaluation process.

Job description. In most cases it should be possible during the interview to describe thoroughly the kind of work assignment the applicant is being interviewed for. This type of information will help the intelligent applicant decide in his own mind whether he is qualified for the work and whether it is the kind of assignment he is interested in.

Almost all research applicants are interested in the growth potential of the position for which they are applying. Every opportunity should be made during the interview to review the company's plans for and interest in fostering this growth. Some of the policies which can be used to promote professional growth and advancement are:

1. On-the-job training programs.
2. Performance appraisals.
3. Encouragement of professional and technical society membership and of active participation in local and national meetings.
4. Organization of special laboratory seminars, which make use wherever possible of guest lecturers of recognized authority.
5. Encouragement of publication.
6. Promotion of visits to other laboratories active in the same fields of research and extending invitations to other scientists.
7. Advanced schooling at company expense.
8. Interproject and interdepartmental transfers to help the professional employee broaden his work experience without looking outside the company.

A discussion of growth potential would not be complete without some reference to the applicant's opportunity for promotion. Too many young men are under the false impression that unless an organization is continually in a rapid state of expansion, the opportunities for advancement will be seriously limited. This is rarely the case. The men who are promoted most rapidly are normally those who devote themselves completely to the job to which they are assigned. On the other hand, the unhappy engineer is generally the one who overestimates his capabilities, and is constantly maneuvering for a promotion for which he is not yet ready.

DECISION AND FOLLOWTHROUGH

Perhaps the most critical area of the evaluation process is the task of reaching a decision on the research applicant. Very often a great deal of pressure has been built up to expand a research program. Under these conditions in particular, but in the general case as well, it is most important to maintain an *objective* attitude toward the applicant. In essence, objectivity can be achieved by conscious consideration of three ground rules during the final evaluation of the research applicant.

1. Avoid searching for the "ideal" man. Especially in many advanced areas of research, experienced individuals or specialists will be very difficult to locate. Thus, a long search for "just the right man" may seriously delay a research program.
2. In all cases, make offers only to qualified applicants. Do not yield to pressure and make offers to applicants who, if hired, would in any way lower the average competence level of the present research staff.
3. Before hiring, compare the applicant with present research personnel. In many cases, it will be much more satisfactory to effect an internal transfer of an existing employee and provide him with some additional training than to bring in the "ideal" man from the outside.

Wherever possible, the expansion of a research staff should be looked upon as an opportunity to raise the average competence level of the organization. Use of the above three ground rules of objectivity should definitely help attain this goal.

The actual decision to hire should be made by a responsible research executive who has interviewed the applicant. The research executive does this in conjunction with a representative of the personnel department. This duty cannot be delegated down the line since a grave responsibility is involved. Both the applicant and the research organization are equally concerned with the equity and the correctness of the decision involved. The applicant's best interests and those of the research organization should not be in conflict since the basic objective of staffing a laboratory should be to maximize the effectiveness of its staff as well as its physical facilities.

After an offer of employment has been made, management must still follow through on the decision made by the applicant. If he declines the offer, then steps should be taken to determine why the applicant did not accept. This is often more easily said than done. Such information can best be obtained by having the personnel manager telephone the applicant and informally discuss the reasons behind his negative decision. Very often such a conversation will provide valuable information which can be applied to future recruiting problems. In other cases, it may turn up a simple misunderstanding on the part of the applicant which when cleared up will enable him to reconsider the initial offer. Too many companies fail to take advantage of this simple technique.

If the applicant accepts the offer, his integration into the research organization should be followed through with care and planning. Initial problem assignments should be made wherever possible to maximize his immediate contribution to the research program. At the same time, his first assignments should be designed to contribute to his future growth potential in the research organization.

The two-way approach to the evaluation of research applicants can be summed up in one word: COURTESY. The way an applicant is treated during this period will more often than not form a lasting impression on him. The courteous, two-way approach to evaluation cannot help but pay off in goodwill toward the company over a period of time.

Conscientiously employed, the philosophy and techniques for selecting researchers which have been discussed here should make easier the task of hiring better-than-average applicants. When an applicant senses that the research organization and its representatives are genuinely concerned with his best interests, he can't help but become more cooperative. This becomes of significant importance since only rarely can a satisfactory evaluation of an applicant be made without his active cooperation. In the final analysis, it must be recognized that no human selection process can ever be foolproof; it can only supplement human judgment and experience for which no substitute exists.

BUILDING THE RESEARCH TEAM •

W. M. HOYT

IN THE PREVIOUS TWO CHAPTERS in this section, we have read about ways to attract to the research organization the type of talent it needs to carry on its work and about methods of selecting from this talent those individuals who possess the most desirable combination of skills and abilities in terms of the organization's needs. The next step, and often a crucial one in the process, is the organization of these skills and abilities into teams or groups to accomplish specific research objectives.

Admittedly, research—which has been defined as the science of discovery—has always been more of an individual effort than has engineering, where a combination of closely integrated diverse abilities is usually needed to arrive at practical answers to highly complex technical problems. However, even research problems, and particularly those in applied research, are usually solved more efficiently by a combination of the talents of several persons than by one person, and in view of the value that today's marketplace puts on the time of individuals with these talents, the efficiency with which research is conducted is an important economic consideration. Because of its importance to industry and Government alike, it is surprising how relatively little is known about the human aspects of conducting research, except what is required in terms of technical capabilities. However, it seems safe to assume that much of the absence of social research on this subject is due to the fact that it was only quite recently that the costs of research began to spiral upward (25 years ago the supply of competent talent exceeded the demand), and thus the practical need for knowledge on this subject has been missing until this time.

Another reason for the absence of much knowledge on this subject may also be its very complexity, for we are dealing here with the manner

W. M. HOYT is Director—Personnel, Univac Division of Sperry Rand Corporation, New York, New York.

in which we should group people having the necessary kinds and amounts of education, experience, and abilities; and if we then add the third dimension of personality factors, in order to achieve a smoothly functioning team, the complexity of the problem is immediately evident. Without making an exhaustive study of the subject, it seems worthwhile to report on two observations in the area of the social sciences before moving on to the area having to do with skills and abilities.

One author[1] identifies one of the dimensions as *inclusion,* or the need to belong, and he found that if the behavior expressed by one individual on a given dimension matches the behavior wanted by his partner in that dimension, their interaction will generally go smoothly. However, if the expressed and wanted behaviors are incompatible, it can be expected that trouble will develop with respect to interpersonal contact. In his study, Shutz formed the hypothesis that differences in compatibility would affect the productivity or efficiency of a group in tasks requiring group cooperation. Experiments he conducted showed this hypothesis to be true; thus he found that compatible groups were significantly more productive than those that were incompatible and that goal achievement (as defined by the group) varies directly with the compatibility of the group members as determined by his FIRO scales.

Another study reports on some social factors related to performance in a research organization.[2] One of the analyses the author made had to do with the relationship between the types and frequency of contact a researcher made in the conduct of his work and his performance on the job. What was being investigated here was related to the work and science orientation of the individual and therefore to his values—and to the point of view from which he looked at a scientific problem, rather than his personal needs as discussed above. Pelz' work indicates that individual performance will be higher under the following conditions:

1. Strong personal emphasis placed upon science-oriented values of using one's abilities, having freedom to pursue original ideas, and making contributions to basic scientific knowledge.

2. Frequent (daily) contact with several scientific colleagues who on the average have been employed in settings different from one's own, who stress different values, and who tend to work in different scientific fields.

3. At the same time, frequent contact with at least one important colleague who has similar professional values.

[1] Shutz, William C., *FIRO: A Three-Dimensional Theory of Interpersonal Behavior,* Rinehart & Company, Inc., New York, 1958.
[2] Pelz, Donald C., *The Sociology of Science,* The Free Press of Glencoe, New York, 1962.

If we think now in terms of skills and abilities that are needed, it is helpful to look at the nature of the work to be done. As we well know, research work is mostly mental, requiring little manual skill. The amount of each depends both on (1) the nature of the science involved and, to some extent, (2) the degree to which the study is of a basic or applied nature. In fact, in some sciences such as mathematics, no manual skills are required at all; but, instead, the differentiation is in terms of creative or theoretical thought versus routine, lower-level mental processes. In contrast to this, in the field of experimental physics, for instance, a considerable amount of manual skill in soldering, metal working, and glass blowing—to name a few—may be required.

It should be obvious, then, that from the viewpoint of the efficient use of the talents and education possessed by the professional personnel to whom is entrusted the research that is to be performed, there should be assigned to help or support these professionals other individuals with lower-level mental abilities or with more highly developed manual skills. The advantages of this combination of professional and technical support personnel are clear: (1) each works continuously in the upper ranges of his particular level of capability, is constantly challenged by his work, and derives a sense of accomplishment and personal growth from it; and (2) lower-level skills are performed by individuals who are paid accordingly, resulting in a lower overall cost of the project. The situation described in the first advantage meets the conditions described in another book which contends that the work itself, responsibility, and advancement were found to be the prime "motivators."[3] The authors reached the following conclusion, which was based on studies they had made of engineers and accountants: "It is primarily these motivators that serve to bring about the kind of job satisfaction and . . . the kind of improvement in performance that industry is seeking in its work force." Result: higher productivity, lower turnover, and lower cost.

Like everything else, providing professional personnel with technical support can be overdone. In other words, there seems to be an optimum ratio of professionals to technicians for each project. To quote the research director of a food company, "If you don't give a research man enough help, you will have a high-grade man doing low-grade work that should be done by lower-paid people. But if you give a good research man too much help, he may just sit at his desk and administer. You have to get your hands dirty to do creative research."

There is another aspect of the effective utilization of professional

<hr />

[3] Herzberg, Frederick, and Others, *Motivation to Work*, John Wiley & Sons, Inc., New York, 1959.

personnel that is worth mentioning: the proper use by these professionals of their support personnel. The following is a quotation from one of the best studies on this problem that I am aware of.[4] Although this report deals with the problem of engineering manpower, some of its conclusions apply equally in the area of scientific personnel engaged in research.

> There is some feeling that engineers lack understanding of the role that supporting personnel play. Mr. D. C. Boulton of the McDonnell Aircraft Corporation has pointed this out. He said, "A great many engineers do not understand clearly the function of a technician, and so do not utilize him properly. They may be confused because an engineer and, usually, a technician both have knowledge of mathematics and physics, though [at] different levels. The difference lies in the way each uses his knowledge. The engineer plans, designs, creates, or carries on research; the technician computes, draws, takes readings, or operates. It is, therefore, evident that for the more effective use of his manpower, a supervisor should know each man and his background." The survey did not reveal any glaring or common misutilization of technicians. However, the implications of the foregoing remarks are clear. Apparently, it is very difficult for an engineer who has spent long years of education and experience learning his profession to understand that someone with lesser background can be expected to do part of his tasks. Or even if he does concede this point, once he is past the major training status of his career, he is very reluctant to let go of the routine and minute details of the work. There can be no question, then, that this is a strong barrier against the full and free use of the various kinds of supporting personnel.
>
> The success with which technicians are used to enhance an engineer's productivity is also dependent on how well the engineer can direct the work of his technicians. Apparently, relatively few engineers have mastered this technique. The executive secretary of a New York engineering society supports this view; [he] remarked, more specifically, that "engineers are more inclined to do the work themselves than to take time to explain or organize the technicians' work."

The report summarizes its conclusions on this point as follows:

1. Industry has generally recognized the value of the use of support personnel. Indeed, their use can contribute dramatically to increasing engineering productivity. However, many companies do not have a conscious, planned, and carefully evaluated approach to the use of such personnel. . . . Companies that recognize the benefits of supporting personnel can do a lot more through the use of such an approach.

2. The most important and basic problem [involved in] getting the best use of engineering aides is that of the engineer's attitude. Generally, engineers do not understand the role of these people. Therefore, they do not use them effectively.

---

[4] Graduate School of Business Administration, Harvard University, *Engineering Manpower: How to Improve Its Productivity*, 1957.

Finally, a research manager must always recognize the human tendency of his scientists to hold on to help, often after that help is no longer needed. When the supply of technical support personnel in an organization is less than the demand, this condition can become particularly critical. The research director of a chemical company has described his solution to this problem as follows:

> Our research laboratory pools its technical assistants for assignments to researchers during a particular project. When the project is finished, the assistant returns to the pool. Under this plan researchers don't feel they "own" a technician; so they aren't tempted to create work in order to justify keeping him. The technicians stay busy and get varied experience. And it's flexible; a technician with specialized knowledge can be assigned to work on a related project, no matter who conducts it.

Specifically, what should be the optimum ratio of professional scientists or engineers to supporting technical personnel in a research project? To answer this question, let us look at some data representing a number of physics research groups in the Univac Engineering Center Research Department at St. Paul, Minnesota (see Table 1).

Project	Professionals	Technical Support	P/T
a	1	1.5	.67
b	2	1.5	1.33
c	2	2	1.00
d	2	0	—
e	2	1	2.00
f	1	1	1.00
g	3	1	3.00
	13	8	1.62

TABLE 1

In contrast to this situation, a typical mathematical research group or programing research group is composed of five to ten professionals, supported by one or two technical personnel. In physical research, then, a realistic ratio of professional to technical would be 1.5 to 1 or possibly 2 to 1, while in the sciences requiring no manual skills, a ratio of 5 to 1 would be more practical. Looking at the composition of a fairly typical section engaged in physics and physical chemistry research from the viewpoint of types and levels of education, we find the situation illustrated in Table 2. In the same way, looking at a mathematics research group, we find it comprised of the individuals shown in Table 3.

Before closing, brief mention should be made of what are rather

Manager		Ph.D.	Physics
Professional Staff	1	Ph.D.	Physics
	1	M.S.	Physics
	1	M.S.	Engineering
	1	B.S.	Chemical Engineering
Technical Support	1	B.S.	Chemistry
	1	Laboratory Technician	

TABLE 2

Manager		Ph.D.	Math
Professional Staff	1	Ph.D.	Math
	1	Ph.D.	Physics
	2	M.S.	Math
	1	M.S.	Philosophy and Logic
	2	B.S.	Math
	1	B.S.	Physics
	1	B.S.	Engineering
Technical Support	1	Programer	
	1	Clerk	

TABLE 3

commonly known as "skills inventories." In order to form the groups or team assigned to a particular project, or even to select the one individual who will be given the task—if it is a one-man project—management must have available to it information on the skills and abilities of its employees. In the smaller organization, this information is often kept in the mind of the manager, and possibly his personnel man. However, the larger the organization, the less practical this method becomes, and in its place a mechanized inventory of skills is used. Modern data-processing equipment is ideal for this purpose.

Many systems for classifying this information have been developed, but it seems appropriate to mention here a system developed recently by the Engineering Manpower Commission of Engineers Joint Council. In this system, four factors are used to identify fully the technical capabilities of an engineer or scientist: education, area of technological competency, product or service, and function. A reasonably complete list has been compiled for each factor, with provision made for expansion as technology changes.

A typical listing for a professional member of a research department might be as follows:

Education:	Physics
Area of technological competence:	Solid State
Product or service (list 3):	Digital computers
	Storage devices
	Display devices
Function:	Research

Naturally, to this information should be added data giving the level of his highest degree in physics and perhaps the year, and also information on the total amount of experience in each of the three product areas listed.

In summary, the most effective research team will be composed of individuals with reasonably compatible personalities, but with different values, possessing a variety of skills and education as required by the project so that each performs rather consistently near the upper limits of his capability in helping the group achieve its goal.

COMPENSATING SCIENTIFIC PERSONNEL •

CHARLES W. G. VAN HORN

W E FREQUENTLY SPEAK OF "REWARDS" for the professional or technical people on our payrolls. True, all of us derive satisfaction from our work which would defy statement in terms of dollars, and perhaps this applies even more to research and scientific personnel than to the rest of us. For the moment, however, let us concern ourselves exclusively with *salary*-centered rewards and let such matters as titles, formal recognition, attendance at professional conclaves, help in obtaining publication, and the opportunity for sabbatical leaves—though admittedly important to the professional man—go by the board.

The problems of compensating research people are not too different from those found in other business areas. In fact, they are so similar that they can generally be handled in the same way as compensation problems throughout the rest of the company. It is well that this is so, because equity from department to department and from group to group is a key consideration in any systematic program of salary administration. And since our problems in all areas are similar, we can use the same "yardsticks," or standards, throughout.

There is a tendency to complicate this process beyond useful return. We hear, for example, that the usual methods for measuring jobs and paying people don't apply to this area. If we are not careful, we will find many reasons why the area can't be dealt with successfully, though experience shows that this is not the case at all. As in all other areas of management, we are constantly looking for better ways to arrive at the answers; but we do not wait for perfection before doing something.

As with all other jobs, compensation for research jobs is based, in order of importance, on job-content measurement, translation of job-content measurements into a salary structure, and the "care and feeding" of these

CHARLES W. G. VAN HORN is General Partner, Edward N. Hay & Associates, Philadelphia, Pennsylvania.

measurements. These criteria have been developed over the years in co-operation with technical and professional people as well as with managers at all levels. They have evolved from a basis of common sense and, I might add, a healthy amount of original skepticism.

JOB-CONTENT MEASUREMENT

Let's consider job measurement first. We use a variety of multiple judgments to arrive at the relation of one job to another, but the process I am most familiar with is, fundamentally, that of direct comparison. Experience has shown that this is made easier by comparing those aspects of a job which are common to all jobs (in varying degrees), rather than having to compare each complete job.

Every job exists for the purpose of accomplishing something useful. To do this, each job calls for three things: know-how ("savvy," or the technical human relations and managerial requirements); problem solving (using your head independently); and accountability (in terms of some specific effect on an identifiable end result of worth to the company). These are the aspects of a job which we consider important and therefore analyze.

In identifying, analyzing, describing, and providing the means for measurement of these things, the objective is to get at the essence, or hard core of the job. Why does it exist? What kind of job is it? Within what general framework and environment does it operate? In the system of management and organization, how freely does the job operate in thinking and doing? And what, exactly, are know-how, problem solving, and accountability?

To aid us in incorporating these aspects into job evaluation, we in our consulting work use guide charts; through these we arrive at the ultimate decision as to where a job fits into the scheme of things with respect to its know-how, problem solving, and accountability. The charts have been particularly useful in dealing with some of the basic problems which confront everyone concerned with the measurement of technical and professional jobs. By using the guide charts, plus the refinement of job-to-job comparisons, appropriate numerical values for each job that is measured are placed on know-how, problem solving, and accountability. This then provides a relative index showing where that particular job fits into the scheme of jobs under study.

One word of caution: do not let money considerations distort your judgment about the relativity of jobs. This is a particular temptation in dealing with technical and professional jobs which currently may be in short supply in the market. Keep the evaluation relationships sound and handle the salary problems in other ways.

Know-how. This involves the question as to how the specialist relates to the administrator and the corollary problem of how high in the salary or evaluation scale a nonadministrative scientific job can rise. Our experience has shown us that there are three subaspects of know-how which can be dealt with separately; using them, we arrive at a single point value for the know-how for a given job. These subaspects are the practical, specialized, or technical know-how required; the need for human skills in motivating people; and the element of functionally diversified and integrated know-how (breadth of management). The know-how chart, representing various degrees of these requirements, recognizes and provides a means for measuring the dual course of development in technical and professional jobs: it starts with the young graduates doing specialized work and advances to a point where some jobs begin to have an administrative or a managerial content while others at the same level remain on the specialized course, emphasizing a high degree of technical skill and unique mastery in the chosen field. This permits us to deal with the so-called dual ladder that we hear so much about in technical and professional circles. In the process of measurement there are no limitations—except those of fact—on how high the specialist can go in relation to the administrator, although the human relations aspect is of course another differentiating element which is brought to bear in determining the final know-how relativity of the two kinds of jobs.

During the course of one of our client seminars for research and development personnel, the consensus seemed to be that the specialist, under most circumstances, could be expected to rise no higher than to within one, or more probably two, levels below the research director. These men, in principle, admitted to no theoretical limitation on the specialist; they were speaking of the practical realities of today's research organizations and needs. Mention was made in our discussion of the high-level specialist, the man with a unique contribution in his chosen field, the "rare bird." However, these research managers felt that an even "rarer bird" was a man who had strong technical qualifications and at the same time had demonstrated considerable managerial abilities.

Problem solving. This is probably the aspect of mental activity most readily associated with technical and professional people. Analyzing, evaluating, reasoning, and arriving at and making conclusions is what they do. The amount of thinking in a job is considered in two dimensions: (1) the relative freedom to think independently which is reflected by the job; and (2) the kinds of problem solving which characterize it. The scope of the second dimension runs from selective memory, a relatively low order of analytical thinking consisting of simple choice, to a high order of creativity in novel, nonrecurring situations characterized by pathfinding. Various levels of these two dimensions are appropriately pictured on the problem-solving guide chart. This particular representation appeals to technical and professional people, and they use it effectively.

Accountability. Here we measure another important freedom—the relative freedom to act independently. Freedom to think in problem solving and freedom to act in accountability are both elements which particularly characterize research jobs, but personnel usually have relatively greater freedom to think and much more limited freedom to act independently. The other dimensions of accountability are the magnitude of the end result most clearly or primarily affected and the nature of the effect—the impact —the job has on that magnitude.

Job description. In addition to these three major aspects of job-content measurement, there is the overall job description, or job analysis, which is an indispensable part of the measurement process. It results from a thoughtful, perceptive interview which has been keyed into the three aspects to be measured; it is not an endless list of duties. The job description also contains, within itself, a list of three important points:

1. Interview notes must be sifted in order to separate the important from the unimportant; they are then rearranged in meaningful, well-chosen words and figures to give the reader a clear understanding of the job.

2. Lengthy descriptions should normally be avoided. If you can't say what you need to say about a given job in a relatively few paragraphs, it may be because you yourself don't fully grasp the key aspects of that job.

3. Claims of job content should not be accepted unless clearly supported in the body of the description. Find out how the interviewee uses what he claims he has to know.

Job descriptions are written in a variety of forms to suit the special needs and desires of a particular company. I like the broad format which starts off with a general statement of why the job exists—how it affects what end results—and then elaborates on this through a narrative statement of the environment which surrounds the job. It then gives some key points about the nature and scope of the job and, finally, rounds out the picture with a carefully sifted and organized list of principal activities necessary to attain the accountability objectives.

I consider the *narrative statement* of the job description to be of prime importance because it is particularly useful in transmitting a clear understanding of technical jobs. In the technical and professional area particularly, there is a danger of describing the job in such general terms that it leaves the reader totally in the dark about the real content; he gets no sense of whether the job is lightweight or heavyweight, or something in between. It is often helpful to use comparatives in these instances, preferably worked into the narrative statement. For example, some years ago when I was studying a group of jobs in analytical chemistry, the laboratory director saw a particular group of analytical chemists' jobs in three categories. In describing the job of the middle group, I said that it was midway between the lower analytical chemists' jobs, which followed prescribed procedures in relatively simple analyses, and those higher jobs which were developed to the point of highly skilled specialization in complex analyses. The laboratory director had explained that he viewed the lower jobs as generally following prescribed procedures with very little, if any, method development work. The middle group, on the other hand, was involved in some of the more complex analyses and did some adaptive work in arranging methods to arrive at the desired results. In contrast to these two groups, the highest level of analytical chemist's job in this particular operation involved a lot more stress on new methodology and not so much analytical work of a repetitive nature.

Another attractive trap to avoid is the practice of suggesting job levels by academic degrees—B.S., M.S., or Ph.D. In place of this dubious crutch, discipline yourself to seek out the job requirement which justifies employing men of these academic levels.

In support of individual job description, it is often very useful to describe the function within which the jobs are organized—a sort of job description of the whole function. I call it a chapter on the function. In describing the research function, for example, an analysis of this sort would highlight such things as the way in which research coordinates with and is integrated into corporate activities; a brief outline of the way research works in that particular company; some explanation of the broad economics of research; and a statement on how the director develops and broadly carries out an economic rationale. It would elaborate on the kinds of research being undertaken, such as fundamental, product-centered, and production-centered. It would identify the corporate controls acting on research and explain how the director uses them, including the control latitude given subordinates. Finally, the analysis might cover the manner in which research activities and findings are communicated throughout the research organization and beyond. Facts such as these, and many more, would give the reader a clear insight into the whole function: the various jobs which make up the research organization would have more meaning when viewed against this background.

In the field of technical and professional jobs there is a great diversity of job content. The nature of jobs varies from the rather structured, routine sort to the very unstructured, creative type. By the thorough methods of analysis I have just outlined, it is possible to point up the differences clearly.

From time to time, industry groups develop standards for job content in the technical area and define various levels of complexity and importance. One such group sees the research job family in six levels. This sort of data is helpful as background material but, if it is not used in a very thoughtful manner, tends to confuse rather than to help. For this reason, there is no substitute for measuring your own situation in terms of what you have rather than trying to impose external criteria on your particular group. If you discipline yourself to discover and measure your own research structure, for example, you not only are measuring what you have but are building a sound base for adjustment to changes as they may occur from time to time.

The question is frequently asked whether there should be a description for each job or whether prototype descriptions can cover groups of closely related jobs. I have found that prototype descriptions are very common and represent a sensible solution to the problems of data gathering, workloads, and subsequent administration. However, jobs should be grouped under single descriptions only after a sufficient sample has been measured and the fact established that a group of jobs represents differences only in kind —not in degree—of difficulty and importance.

There is no need to discuss the mechanics of job measurement. A wealth of material is available on this subject, and the principles are fairly well established. We still occasionally run into the "doubting Thomases" who say that technical and professional jobs cannot be measured as other jobs are measured. In response, I would say that whenever you meet someone else, you immediately begin to make judgments about him and that the same thing applies to his job. These judgments are being made all the time in one way or another; it is our objective in this work to bring to the task a greater degree of orderliness and consistency, so that the results can be produced and explained on the basis of facts if and when they should ever be challenged.

Job evaluation. In order to build a consistent relationship, it is necessary to employ job evaluation—the measurement of technical and professional jobs. The most advantageous time to do this is when you are evaluating jobs in other areas of the business. If technical and professional jobs are evaluated separately, the relationships developed may appeal to research management; however, difficulties frequently arise when an effort is made to coordinate them with those in other company departments. When new jobs are created or existing jobs change sufficiently to be re-evaluated, it is good practice to relate them to an overall framework representing the entire organization rather than just the research or scientific function. This eliminates the possibility—and it is a real possibility—of the relationships between jobs in various functions drifting apart over a period of time.

SALARY STRUCTURE

The question is often asked: should we develop grades for the salary structure? This is a matter of choice, personal preference, or simply continuing a practice already in effect and widely accepted by the organization. A number of our clients merely let each job carry its own salary range (without grades) corresponding to the evaluation point score for the particular job.

The salary structure now shows only the degree of internal salary equity. It should be compared with appropriate external criteria to show where it is in relation to the rest of the business world—or that segment of it with which you choose to be compared. Here the salary administrator draws upon a number of survey reports conducted on an annual basis; among these are the AMA compensation surveys and the Los Alamos surveys, with their families of curves based on year-since-degree. This material is very helpful; however, as the surveys themselves point out, it must be used with caution and discretion.

Measuring for salary structure. A single salary structure is most desirable for the company and, in my experience, has proved both attainable and workable. However, by using *scattergram data,* the salary administrator gains insight into the possibility of variation in salary treatment between kinds of jobs in the company. This will be important in developing a salary structure from the job evaluation and existing salary information. When the data represent a large enough volume of jobs, each function can be plotted on a separate scattergram, thus showing the diversity which exists between functional salary practices. Other groupings can also be investigated: for example, all scientific and technical jobs (which, no matter where they may be found in the organization, can be placed under one heading); control jobs; jobs involving functional specialization; production, sales, and administrative jobs. It is surprising how often technical and professional jobs show up as a group at the midpoint; seldom do they have a favorable position relative to other functions.

Minimum and maximum salary limits are then constructed around a line of central tendency. A 50 per cent salary spread from minimum to maximum is fairly common for technical and professional jobs.

In several cases, top technical managers have expressed fear about the limiting nature of salary standards. Subsequent investigation has shown that they keep their men low in the range and fail to use even the administrative latitude available to them. Occasionally, these situations result from an unwillingness on the part of managers to recognize that younger men are holding down jobs at an acceptable level of performance. This occurs particularly in technical activities involving fairly new disciplines where it is almost exclusively the younger men who have the know-how. Some companies periodically conduct *individual surveys* for their own guidance as supplements to the annual surveys already mentioned. In this regard, there is no substitute for having the salary administrator or his representative sit down with his counterparts in other companies and actually discuss and evaluate the jobs which are being measured. This allows the cooperating parties to clarify any points of misunderstanding. It also enables them to discuss particular facets of the participating companies which might affect job content.

It is preferable to get sufficient data to enable the participating companies to construct salary lines of central tendency rather than simply to compare data on a job-by-job basis. This will reveal clearly what the companies are doing as a consistent practice, at all salary levels, and it will tend to eliminate the job whose pay, for reasons identified with the particular firm, is either abnormally high or low.

I have found it very helpful to use some device such as the guide charts to insure reliable, consistent comparisons. By this method the jobs of the other companies can be stated in one's own evaluation terms, and it will not be necessary to find matching jobs. This is where the functional chapter mentioned earlier helps to place the companies in the proper overall relations. It helps to identify, for example, the relative sophistication of the research activities being compared and enables one to consider the varying philosophies which influence job content in the participating companies.

The magnitude aspect of accountability also allows one to recognize and measure jobs of similar kinds but of different dimensions. Another advantage of this method is that, once one has carefully established with cooperating companies the evaluation relationships of a job, ranging from low to high, from various functional parts of the organization, the survey can easily be brought up to date by reporting on the salary movements since the last inquiry. As long as the contents of the sample jobs have not changed materially, the evaluations will still be valid. (Remember that it is job content which counts, not job title.)

The possible problems of a salary structure. In all this I am stressing concern with the whole salary structure because I believe that this is the soundest way to look at technical and professional compensation. There are times when we stress too much the matter of starting salaries, or how much we have to pay a Ph.D., for example. These are admittedly difficult problems, but they should always be considered with due regard for the overall salary structure.

A structure with a 50 per cent spread between minimum and maximum salary gives considerable latitude in administering salaries. Many companies use this range in a judicious way to meet the market. For example, one large firm with varied technical and professional jobs adjusts to the realities of a situation in this way: physicists and chemists at a certain level fall in the same salary range; however, the accepted recruiting rate for the one is higher than for the other. After much soul searching, the company has simply decided to use the upper part of the range, as necessary, for the jobs in short supply and higher demand. It watches the situation closely and makes appropriate adjustments as needed, since it has been management's experience that specific shortages move around over the years from one scientific discipline to another and that the problem, furthermore, is not unique to research and engineering.

The soundness of a salary structure is sometimes questioned when technical and professional turnover seems to be too high, especially if a particularly valuable man leaves. It may be in such cases that the salary structure is inadequate, but there are other possibilities to be considered before getting panicky. It is well recognized that many technical and professional people advance in compensation by changing jobs. The fact to be pinned down is whether a particular change was a lateral move or one that represented a step up to a job with more content. I have found that the latter is more frequently the case.

Similarly, in situations where a potential Ph.D. recruit has been lost because another company offered him more money, it is helpful to find out what kind of job the other company plans to use him in. For example, you may simply have wanted to add him to your staff of Ph.D.'s, whereas the other company may be giving him a chance to create a new department or function. Such facts, along with an understanding of the circumstances, help to reduce the confusion and faulty conclusions which sometimes surround this kind of disappointment.

CARE AND FEEDING OF A JOB-MEASURED SALARY STRUCTURE

There are many shades of opinion as to whether employees should know how their jobs are rated and be familiar with salary ranges. In my opinion, a principal factor in assuring the maximum effectiveness of the compensation dollar is good communication with the people affected. Management often does a less than satisfactory job in this area because it either overlooks the importance of communication or is concerned about the problems, imaginary or real, which might arise from telling people about the principles and methods used in arriving at compensation.

I believe that technical and professional personnel, along with the people in other areas of the business, should know that the company has an orderly method of establishing and maintaining salary standards. Sufficient details should be supplied so that they can have confidence in what the company is doing. I believe that this information should be revealed, preferably, in a manner which fits the company's characteristics and its means of communicating such material. I know of no organization which has had difficulty as a result of going that far; there are still many more companies which hold back the information. Happily, the tendency seems to be to aim at going "all the way" in imparting job and salary information, to keep this in mind as an objective to be reached in due time and under the right circumstances.

Obviously, however, in order to administer salaries effectively, there must be some form of performance appraisal to indicate where the individual fits into the range for his job. This is a problem which has been particularly difficult in the technical and professional area, where much work remains to be done. Meanwhile, the job description is a useful vehicle for gaining a deeper insight into individual performance. It can be used effectively as a communicating link between the job holder and his superior; moreover, as already mentioned, it serves as a foundation for the establishment of specific criteria against which performance can be measured, at least qualitatively and, in many cases, quantitatively as well. There are some jobs which are so unstructured and free-wheeling that an overall judgment about performance is about as much as the superior can manage at present, but he *must* go this far in any event. Together, the technical man and his boss can develop criteria which have meaning to them and which can be used as a yardstick for performance; at review time it is, of course, easier to discuss a man's performance in terms of specifics rather than talk around generalities.

EXTRA INCENTIVES IN COMPENSATION

Finally, there is the matter of extra incentives in compensating technical and professional personnel. In any consideration of the problems involved, three criteria must be borne in mind.

1. *The criterion of success.* The employee's extra efforts must produce something of worth to the company. If money is to be paid out, this means that profits must be generated from which the rewards can be taken.
2. *The criterion of opportunity.* By their very design, various jobs have different opportunities to contribute to the success of the enterprise. We use the accountability evaluation as the best index to this relativity.
3. *The criterion of performance.* This answers the question, "How well did the incumbent measure up to his opportunity?"

These three criteria are sound bases for any extra-incentive program.

With regard to technical and professional jobs, there are at least three forms of money awards in the extra-incentive class:

1. The reward for a significant *one-time contribution*. A scientist has provided an important breakthrough in his field, for example. In its typical form, the award results from committee judgment as to the value of the contribution and who should be included in recognition of the attainment. This type of compensation, I believe, should be a part of any technical and professional program.

2. Extra-incentive compensation in the form of *profit sharing*. This usually occurs as a programed distribution of profits based on eligibility criteria to be shared on the basis of relative salary. While it is undoubtedly a general stimulus to better effort, there is a drawback in that cause and effect in producing the result are often hard to relate to each other.

3. A refinement of the more general profit-sharing plan is the use of the three yardsticks, *success, opportunity, and performance*—individual or group—in an effort to relate cause and effect more closely and so make it possible for those responsible for profits to have a share in them. This is very common in executive compensation, but I have not seen many applications beamed directly to technical and professional personnel.

The research managers with whom I have talked like these ideas but feel inadequate, on the whole, in making compensation based on differences in performance palatable and justifiable to their staffs. This is one of the challenges we all face in rewarding technical and professional people appropriately. It is an area in which we need to be much more thoughtful and creative.

THE CURVE APPROACH TO THE
COMPENSATION OF SCIENTISTS •

EDWARD A. SHAW

DURING THE YEARS FOLLOWING World War II, a new approach to the compensation of scientists emerged in such organizations as the University of California's Los Alamos Scientific Laboratory, Hughes Aircraft Company, and Space Technology Laboratories. The new technique—which reputedly had its genesis at the Bell Telephone Laboratories in the 1930's —has been variously identified by such names as "the maturity curve," "the career curve," "the octile system," and "the individual contributor approach."[1]

Regardless of designation, the several curve programs have in common a philosophy and related methodology that represent a significant departure from the familiar classification systems. Traditionally, classification systems employ classical position analysis and evaluation techniques. The curve approach, on the other hand, relates salary to the variables of educational attainment, maturity or experience, and relative job performance, making no direct reference to actual position responsibilities.

It should be emphasized that this description is of the curve system in its raw form and that there is a great deal of variation in the practical form and application of the curve approach. This variation ranges from the use of a curve merely as a descriptive market reference to its use as a mechanism for arriving at individual salary determinations. Some compensation managers will claim that the maturity factor has absolutely no bearing in their curve system and that salary apportionment is at management discre-

[1] See, for example, Sibson, Robert E., *Wages and Salaries: A Handbook for Line Managers*, American Management Association, New York, 1960, pp. 169-174. The author discusses two variants which he identifies as the "career curve" and "individual contributor curve" respectively. In West Coast aerospace and electronics firms, "maturity curve" seems to have become the most common designation.

EDWARD A. SHAW is Staff Head—Compensation Programs, System Development Corporation, Santa Monica, California.

tion through such control devices as the salary increase budget. On the other hand, many compensation managers will attempt to somehow integrate position evaluation and job criteria with their curve programs. Such differences from one curve approach to another will subsequently be discussed in some detail, but for the moment it is sufficient merely to indicate the range of this variation. It is more important to appreciate the major shift in emphasis that the curve system has brought to formal salary determination processes.

THE POSTWAR EXPERIENCE

The historical origins of the curve approach are not entirely clear, but one gains the impression that its early use occurred somewhat independently and in varying forms at several organizations. This being the case, it is difficult to pinpoint without some speculation the basic forces behind the evolution and development of curve programs. However, based on the historical facts that are known, as well as an analysis of current problems in scientific compensation, it is possible to make some pertinent observations and deductions.

First, the curve approach is basically a phenomenon of the period after World War II and accompanied the growth of scientific research and development. The increase of defense contracts and the concomitant surge in demand for large numbers of engineers and scientists also encouraged the use of the technique. Shortly after the close of the war, the Los Alamos Scientific Laboratory, an Atomic Energy Commission contractor, put into use a curve system for compensating its scientific personnel. In doing so, the Los Alamos management wished to create an environment compatible with scientific research and emulating, to an extent, the academic environment of top-flight universities. It was, apparently, also believed that application of the classical salary techniques would not be entirely consistent with this aim.

Throughout the late 1940's and early 1950's more organizations adopted the curve approach for compensating their scientific staffs. For the most part, these organizations could be characterized as being small- to medium-sized laboratories. A number of them were nonprofit organizations doing work related to the national interest. But there were, in addition, other users of this new compensation technique. Major industrial firms such as Hughes Aircraft Company and General Electric had also developed curve systems for compensating their scientific personnel.

Undoubtedly, the initial motivation for the adoption of some form of the curve approach was the goal of maintaining a creative atmosphere conducive to scientific research. This was based on the contention that removal of position and organization restraints associated with classification systems would promote self-actualization and creativity in the scientist. However, other factors also played a part in encouraging the spread of curve systems. One of these was the ever increasing shortage of engineers and scientists. The inadequate number of qualified personnel created a number of problems from the salary administration point of view. For example, many organizations instituted college recruiting practices in an effort to stockpile technical graduates. Students frequently were hired directly off the campus many months before their graduation and with no specific job in mind. This practice is no longer as common as it once was. However, the main point is that a condition precedent to classical position analysis and evaluation is a well-defined set of duties and responsibilities. When no such condition existed, and in the absence of other scales of reference, the best an employer could do was to evaluate job potential based on observations of relevant individual qualifications. This set of circumstances and practices was not limited to the new graduate. It applied to senior scientists and engineers as well.

Even when an employer could offer a position with specific duties, quite frequently he found that the salary range established by the classical methods had to give way to the upward pressure on salaries in the scientific and engineering labor markets. Again, this conflict between salaries established in the labor market and those established by internal job evaluation plans applied not only to the new college graduate level but to all scientific and engineering levels. Evaluation points assigned to technical positions often would not result in a salary high enough to meet labor market demands. On the other hand, internal administrative problems arose if such positions were given the same evaluation as other positions in a company but were paid a higher salary as a result of the market pressures.

This conflict, however, generally could be resolved by the simple expedient of establishing a separate salary structure for the scientific and engineering positions.[2] Even then, extremely difficult mechanical problems occurred in applying the classical salary methods to scientists and engineers. Formal position analysis, preparation of position descriptions, and position evaluation were techniques which did not readily lend themselves to application in highly technical areas, particularly where jobs had ill-defined limits and the technology was very new or rapidly changing.

[2] For discussions bearing on this practice, see Otis, Jay L., *The Relationship of the Relative Importance of Functions to Salary Levels Within a Company,* Bulletin No. 30, California Institute of Technology, Pasadena, 1959 and Livernash, Robert E., "The Internal Wage Structure," in *New Concepts in Wage Determination,* McGraw-Hill Book Company, New York, 1957, pp. 140-172.

Perhaps it would not have been impossible to use the classical techniques in these areas, but the staff work required was so extensive—especially in organizations where the scientists and engineers were hired in mass numbers—that the anticipated costs were frequently prohibitive. Therefore, a turn toward a technique such as the curve approach, which on the face of it seemed simpler and far less expensive to administer, was a natural outgrowth of this situation. Furthermore, the curve approach had considerable flexibility of application when it involved such internal processes as personnel transfer or reassignment.

In addition to the problem areas discussed, there were other considerations that militated against the use of classical methods. Certainly there was some lack of acceptance, both by scientists and scientific management, of the validity of existing evaluation techniques. In the same vein, there was some lack of confidence in a nonscientific job analyst's understanding and judgment insofar as scientific jobs were concerned. More implicit than expressed was a feeling that the engineer or scientist, as a professional, should be viewed in light of his personal qualifications rather than his job duties. Such status implications in certain organizational environments have been a significant barrier to the use of evaluation plans.

It was probably just such problems which led Los Alamos and other organizations to a curve approach. All of these difficulties, in greater or lesser degree, continue to exist in the contemporary setting, and though many firms have tried and rejected the curve system, it appears that this technique—in one or another of its forms—has been gaining in favor as a tool to cope with these problems.

CURVE DERIVATION AND APPLICATIONS

The curve approach, in the usual case, is based on the premise that salary growth is related to educational attainment, job performance, and maturity factors—that is, years of applicable experience, age, or years since receipt of the bachelor's degree. Typically, the curves themselves are depicted in a fashion similar to that shown in Exhibit 1.

The actual derivation process is normally based upon labor market surveys.[3] These may be quite general or quite specific regarding such things as field of specialization, degree level, and the like. However, for the purpose of developing the curves, the degree of specificity makes no

[3] A few of the better-known national surveys based on the curve concept are the Massachusetts Institute of Technology's survey of research and development personnel, the Los Alamos Scientific Laboratory's survey of general scientific personnel, and System Development Corporation's surveys of human factors scientists, computer programing personnel, and operations research scientists. All of these surveys have been conducted annually for several years.

Hypothetical Curves

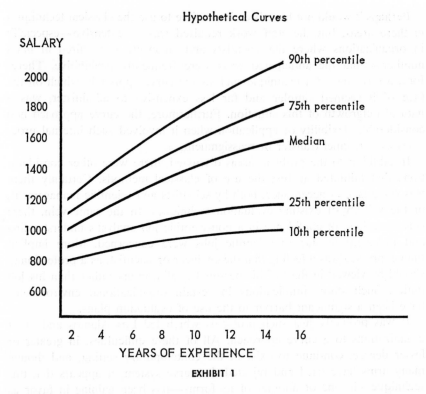

YEARS OF EXPERIENCE

EXHIBIT 1

difference, for the mechanical procedure remains the same. The process simply consists of collecting the individual salaries reported by the survey participants, arranging them in a frequency distribution according to experience or some other measure of maturity, and then smoothing the raw data into a family of curves by applying the least-squares statistical technique to obtain paths of best fit.

Clearly, the mechanical procedure is a simple one. However, there are numerous judgmental and policy considerations attending the use of the curve approach that are quite complex. For one thing, conducting a reliable, comprehensive survey is time consuming and expensive. As a result, existing surveys tend to be limited either to major fields, such as engineering, or to the general scientific population, as is the case with the Los Alamos and M.I.T. surveys. This, of course, creates a problem for companies with scientific personnel in more specialized areas such as the human factors field or operations research. Or perhaps a survey is available for a special branch of the scientific workforce, but it does not apply to a particular firm's competitive industry and environment.

Therefore, quite early in the process, a decision has to be made as to whether an organization will use an existing survey or conduct one of its own. This decision cannot be separated from the consideration that is unquestionably most important of all—namely, how the organization intends to use the curve approach in its compensation program. The discussion that follows illustrates this point and is descriptive of some curve applications.

Basically, there are two general uses that can be made of salary curves. One is as a mechanism to guide salary determinations for the individual scientist. The other is as a reference for assessing the firm's salary position in the labor market. In the first case, the curves tend to act as a control device in much the same manner as salary-grade rate ranges do in a classification system. For any given scientific population, there is a range of salaries for each unit of maturity. Referring once again to Exhibit 1, it may be seen that the range of salaries is described by the 10th and 90th percentiles at the extremes; the median, 25th, and 75th percentiles represent intermediate check points. There is no consistent practice among firms as to the number of curves derived. It may be 7, 8, 10, or even 100, depending on the degree of specificity that the firm wishes to attain.

It should be made eminently clear that, at this juncture, the curves are descriptive rather than prescriptive. The only way in which the curves can become useful guides for the individual salary determination process is through the introduction of some type of quality-rating system. Whether this system is a performance rank, reverse-layoff list, or a ranking of combined factors such as performance, potential, and overall qualifications, it is of the highest importance to the curve approach. It is the main variable in determining what the individual's salary level and relative growth rate are to be in relation to other personnel in the same discipline and at the same maturity level.

Thus far, then, it can be seen that individual salary determinations are a function of both descriptive market curves and a quality-rating system. But the matter is not really as simple as this appears to be. For instance, decisions have to be made as to whether there will be a family of curves for each degree level or whether there will only be one family of curves for all degrees combined. Likewise, it must be decided whether to derive a set of curves for each discipline area or to have a combined set of curves for all scientific disciplines in the company. These considerations are in turn related to the previously mentioned question of whether an organization is to use an existing salary survey or conduct one of its own.

In the typical organization, the curve approach is probably less influential in the individual salary determination process than it is in the companywide process. Many firms depend heavily on the curves in order to arrive at their salary increase budgets or to evaluate their position in the relevant labor market. In the compilation of merit budgets, the procedure is essentially a mechanical one. Firms usually measure the year-to-year growth resulting from an added year of experience on the curve plus the upward movement of curves due to economic and inflationary factors, average this movement, statistically weight it by the company's scientific population for each level of maturity, and thereby arrive at a salary increase budget for the coming year. Naturally, if the organization feels that its market position is either too high or too low in certain areas, it will bring such considerations to bear in arriving at a final figure.

In addition to their use in the derivation of annual salary increase budgets, the curves may be effectively employed to define an organization's labor market position. For example, a company may develop internal maturity curves for its own scientific personnel and superimpose these on the survey curves—and thereby determine with relative accuracy the organization's competitive position. In fact, overall medians can be computed and direct comparisons made between the survey and corporate averages. In cases where the problem of small samples precludes the development of company curves, a scatter of actual salaries in the firm can be plotted against the survey curves. Based on such comparisons, adjustments to the firm's competitive position can readily be made.

It is possible to refine this technique so that the salary positions of individual departments within a firm can also be related to the external labor market. A company may decide, for example, that the average salaries of its research engineers should coincide with the 75th percentile of the survey, while those of its other engineers should fall at the 50th percentile. These policy decisions can then be implemented through direct comparisons with the appropriate set of survey curves.

Not only are the curves helpful in comparing central tendency, but they are also useful for making assessments of what the dispersion of salaries in an organization should be. To illustrate, a company might decide that the distribution of salaries paid to engineers throughout the firm should approximate the distribution of salaries paid in the external labor market. This can be achieved by providing that 10 per cent of the salaries paid by the firm will be below the 10th percentile of the survey, 15 per cent between the 10th and 25th percentiles, 25 per cent between the 25th and 50th percentiles, and so on—paralleling the external labor market at each selected juncture. Such a plan is dependent on an organization's having a relatively large and homogeneous sample of scientists. Otherwise the exercise becomes rather meaningless. Again, the same technique can be applied to individual departments within a company. For instance, management might decide that the research unit should have 50 per cent of its salaries above the 75th percentile of the survey, while other scientific operations could have only 25 per cent above this point.

Merit budgets, median-curve comparisons, and distributional controls in the curve approach have the same intent and effect as rate ranges, "compa-ratios," and midpoint controls have in the classification system. Stated simply, there are controls and guides in the curve system just as there are in the classification approach. The forms of the constraints and the philosophy behind them are somewhat different in the curve approach, but it should not be hastily assumed that the new system is deficient in the control devices which can be used.

This discussion of curve applications has, of necessity, been fairly general. There are many refinements which can be introduced, and the main intent here has been to develop a frame of reference and to outline the basic techniques and philosophy of the curve approach.

PROBLEMS OF THE CURVE APPROACH

The curve approach to compensation of scientists is a controversial one. Many compensation managers damn it; many others have high praise for it. As is usually the case, this technique is probably deserving of neither extreme; there should be, however, some discussion of the principal draw-backs and difficulties associated with this system and an evaluation of its effectiveness.

The curve approach has a number of problems that are common to the entire compensation field. Take, for example, difficulties that are encoun-tered in the conduct of surveys: the complexities of survey design and con-struction, the problems of small samples, inaccurate reporting of survey data, and similar hazards. Taken together, the accumulated error intro-duced by such factors undoubtedly reduces the reliability of the survey. Likewise, a meaningful performance-rating system is critical to the effec-tive functioning of the curve system—as well as the classification system. This, of course, is a whole problem area in itself.

Beyond such difficulties of a general nature there are, in addition, those which are unique to the curve approach. Consider, first, the maturity factor to be selected and used. Obviously an employer does not require maturity for its own sake but, rather, for what it represents in terms of an employee's ability to handle the employer's problems and meet his work requirements. Maturity is nothing more than a convenient and tangible measure of ability. But which is the best measure? Chronological age is quite easily calculated, but is probably least meaningful from the point of view of "employee worth." Years since receipt of B.S. degree is more specific but makes no allowance for experience received before the bachelor's degree, time periods since graduation when experience was nonprofessional in nature (military service, for instance), and experience gained by those few individuals who have become professional scientists without having obtained a degree. Some firms attempt to take these factors into account and develop a theoretical degree date or "equivalent B.S." for purposes of calculating years since B.S. degree. The factor that is most relevant and at the same time most difficult to calculate and apply is professional experience. For example, a set of criteria, which inevitably is controversial, has to be developed in order to evaluate professional experience. Further, it must be determined whether the evaluation is to include all professional experience or just experience that is directly applicable to the scientist's activities. If it is to be the latter, additional salary difficulties develop when the man moves from one field of specialization to another. A typical problem case is the senior engineer who goes into operations research work. His operations research experience starts from zero, and quite frequently this would put his salary for that maturity level in stratospheric reaches.

An entirely different area of difficulty has to do with curve forecasting. If an organization is reviewing salaries in October and the survey curves are as of the previous January, there is obviously a need to project the curves forward in order to stay current with the labor market. This extrapolation is generally based on the curve growth rate shown in the most recent survey. But in Exhibit 2—a set of median curves taken from a national survey of one scientific field—we can see what would have occurred if the 1960 curve had been forecast on the basis of the 1958-59 growth. The 1960 extrapolation would have been considerably different than the actual result. Obviously, part of this problem stems from factors unrelated to the labor market, such as sampling changes and perturbations resulting from the statistical technique.

A corollary problem even larger than forecasting is the administration of a salary program when the curve behavior is as shown in Exhibit 2. For example, strict adherence to the curves in 1960 theoretically would have meant a salary decrease for individuals with seven years' or more experience. In such instances, alternative solutions to annual curve administration have to be sought. These usually take the form of a moving-average growth rate. To illustrate, the 1963 curve might be calculated by averaging the growth rates for the 1958-62 curves, the 1964 curve would be derived from the 1959-63 curves, and so on.

A further difficulty in the curve approach is that it provides no logical solution to the problem of establishing compensation levels for scientific personnel who are not being used in their fields of specialization. The curve

Median Salary Curves: 1958-62

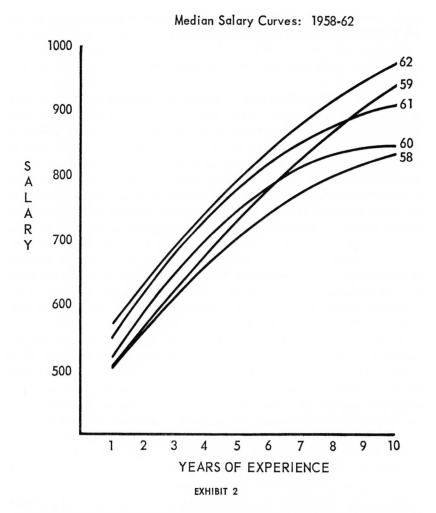

EXHIBIT 2

system assumes that the scientist is engaged in scientific activity. But in many cases, scientists take on administrative assignments or planning functions which are actually unrelated to scientific operations.

On the other hand, there is a problem associated with personnel who do not possess the usual qualifications. Frequently, these individuals are engaged in true scientific endeavor and should be placed on the curve program, even though they do not possess a degree or are lacking in other areas. The real difficulty is to separate them from similar individuals who, it may be claimed, are doing scientific work but in actuality are basically senior technicians. The status and other advantages of being on the scientific staff create considerable pressure to put marginal cases on the curve program. Since the usual classification restraints are absent, it is difficult to maintain control in this area.

ADVANTAGES AND LIMITATIONS—AN ASSESSMENT

Clearly, the basic advantages of the curve approach lie in the several areas which were discussed earlier. First, it is a system that provides the flexibility needed in the scientific research and development milieu. It does not impose predetermined or artificial job constraints on the scientist but, rather, allows him to expand his activities within the limits of his own creative ability. Therefore, salary administraton by the curve method is results-oriented, and it rewards contribution. In a related connection, the curve approach is more acceptable to the scientist as a professional person. Further, from the viewpoint of management and the salary administrator, the curve system is less expensive and easier to administer than the classification technique. Finally, this approach recognizes the shortage in the scientific labor market and the disrupting effect that such shortages have on evaluation plans. Economic studies have shown that internal job evaluation systems cannot operate effectively when they conflict with rates established in the labor market.[4]

However, these advantages of the curve approach do not become operative automatically. For example, a decision has to be made as to which scientific labor market to survey. Even though the theoretical economic model assumes, for analytical purposes, that a single rate clears the market, in actual practice it is not that precise and in the everyday market situation there is actually a range of rates.[5] This range of rates broadens with various factors, but most particularly with the type of industry.[6] The point that needs to be emphasized is that company managements often have much more latitude than they choose to exercise with regard to scientific labor market salaries.

Beyond this consideration, there are the previously discussed problems of a procedural nature that attend the application of the curve approach. Furthermore, the particular history and environment of the individual organization cannot be ignored. A salary structure has a real existence outside of the compensation manual. It has both sociological and psychological significance and, as a result, it is generally quite difficult to change

[4] Kerr, Clark, and Fisher, Lloyd, "Effects of Environment and Administration on Job Evaluation," Harvard Business Review, May 1950, pp. 77-96.

[5] Lester, Richard A., "A Range Theory of Wage Differentials," Industrial and Labor Relations Review, July 1952, pp. 483-500.

[6] Dunlop, John T., "The Task of Contemporary Wage Theory," in New Concepts in Wage Determination, McGraw-Hill Book Company, New York, 1957, pp. 131-139.

a firm's historical salary relationships and differentials. In older organizations, which have had classification systems for a long while, this factor has a distinct influence when the curve approach is introduced into the organization.

Finally, and most important, the underlying assumption of the curve approach is that the individual scientist is a productive resource. The term "maturity curve" is unfortunate because it gives the wrong connotation. Obviously the curve approach, within certain limits, relies on maturity per se to play a part in both individual and companywide salary determination processes. But in the final analysis, the individual's contribution is the most important variable in this system. To this extent, the curve approach is no different than the classical method.

This being the case, it becomes apparent that the curve system is really dependent on effective personnel utilization and, as a corollary, some type of meaningful quality-rating system. Given these, the inherent benefits of the curve approach can be taken advantage of and its limitations minimized. But if these elements are lacking, the curve technique will leave much to be desired.

CONTROLLING RESEARCH WORK

CREATIVITY IN INDUSTRIAL RESEARCH •

JOHN R. HINRICHS

CREATIVITY. What is it? Where does it come from? How can it be identified? What fosters and encourages it? These are questions which go to the core of the problem of productivity in scientific research. They are questions which have been asked increasingly in recent years. And, as we shall see, they are questions which are extremely difficult to answer directly without stating certain reservations and exceptions.

There are two basic reasons why creativity has become a catchword as well as an issue of serious national concern in the 1960's. First, it has become strikingly clear that the balance of forces in the Cold War between East and West hinges largely on technological change. The rate of technological change over the past few decades staggers the imagination; prospects are for an even more rapid rate of change in the future. In blunt point of fact, the survival of our way of life depends on creative technological innovation to maintain both our nation's military superiority as well as our economic vitality.

In addition, managers of many business organizations are vitally concerned with scientific creativity for a somewhat different though related reason. They realize that many of the products on which their profits will depend in the 1970's are today no more than ideas being created and developed and elaborated and tested in their research laboratories. And they realize that the company which does not develop and sustain a flow of creative new ideas will have difficulty remaining healthy in the increasingly competitive business world.

Scientific research is the Johnny-come-lately of the American industrial scene, and it is still suffering growing pains. Now in its adolescence, it is searching for ways to minimize and ultimately to resolve the conflict resulting from the bringing together of its two antecedent strains: business

---

JOHN R. HINRICHS is Personnel Research Associate, Data Processing Division, International Business Machines Corporation, White Plains, New York.

organization and the social system of science. Although science is a relatively new phenomenon in industry, it has grown to the point where industrial research is now big business. And because of the enormous amounts of money which industry is pouring into research, research managers are increasingly under pressure to produce. This pressure is intensified by business competition and by consumer demands for new and better products.

Thus it is that those who offer ways and means of increasing scientific creativity and productivity have an especially eager audience among industrial research managers. In such a climate of concern and pressure, attention to the concept of creativity begins to assume many of the aspects of a fad. But in an area such as this where the stakes are so high, fadism can be extremely costly and, in the national security aspect, disastrous.

In this chapter we will discuss some of the current theorizing and research which is being done in the area of creativity, particularly as it applies to scientific research in industry. Our goal will be to provide a firm foundation—one removed from the influence of fadism—from which the issue of creativity in industrial research can be considered. We will attempt to sample the flavor of some of the "popular" writings dealing with research productivity and administration and then to evaluate them in the light of more rigorous research and theory in the area of scientific creativity.

THE "POPULAR" LITERATURE ON RESEARCH ADMINISTRATION

Almost universally, those who write about industrial research productivity and administration bear the mark of the reformer. The general consensus seems to be that something is wrong, that industry has not matured sufficiently to conduct scientific research in an efficient and effective manner. And unless industry abandons its archaic approaches, the thinking seems to go, there is little hope of achieving much in the way of truly creative scientific accomplishment. By and large, a relatively few observations and generalizations about scientists and industrial research form the basis for recommendations for more effective research management.

SCIENTISTS ARE "DIFFERENT"

Most writers on the subject seem to feel that scientific and engineering personnel are somehow "different" from other employees and have to be treated accordingly. The differences are usually attributed to work habits and attitudes built up in the process of attaining a professional education. The argument generally states: (1) a scientist's work is primarily governed by professional standards, rather than by organizational objectives; (2) as a result of their university training and the traditions of science, scientists have an ingrained propensity to work alone; (3) the logic applied in science is quite different from the logic applied in business; and (4) creativity implies, and depends on, nonconformity.

After reading only a few articles in this vein, we are left with the distinct impression that, in bringing scientists into industry, management has acquired a group of prima donnas who could quite conceivably be more of a problem than an asset. And, to be sure, if a company attempted to provide in full measure all of the conditions which top scientists generally say they want in a job, they would probably go bankrupt. For instance, one survey listed 13 basic job factors desired by scientists:

1. Freedom to publish their work and to discuss it with other members of the scientific community.
2. Opportunity to associate with and be stimulated by high-caliber colleagues.
3. A technically trained management.
4. Freedom to choose the problems or projects on which they are to work.
5. A company with a reputation for scientific advancement.
6. A research director and staff with first-rate reputations as scientists.
7. Adequate facilities, resources, and lower-level technical assistance.
8. Opportunity for advancement and flexibility in advancement policies.
9. A good salary.
10. Security.
11. Suitable living conditions.
12. Individual treatment.
13. An opportunity to continue formal education while working.

The interesting thing about these contentions that technical men are different is that there are several commentators who take the opposite position and whose conclusions seem to be based on relatively objective study of the attitudes and values of research personnel. For example, a survey of more than 3,500 scientists and engineers contradicted the popular contention that scientists belong to a strange breed and should be left alone and treated with kid gloves. Among other things, this survey found that scientists in industry: (1) want to work under relatively close administrative controls, (2) have an urgent need to know precisely what management requires of them, (3) exhibit the same personal traits found generally in ambitious nonscientific people, and (4) resent being categorized as business freaks.

Other commentators concede that research and development people as a group are generally younger, less experienced, and better educated than other types of company personnel; but they point out that these differences are to be expected because of the relative newness of research in industry. Thus they feel that there should not be any special attitude toward scientific researchers on the part of management. The career problems and gripes of top scientists are the same as for any worker: recognition, information on what is going on, efficiency in the way of facilities to do the job, definite assignments, and professional status.

On balance, we are left with a rather confused picture. Some "experts" feel that scientists are basically different from most other industrial employees and require different treatment, while others contend that such differences are largely overstated.

INDUSTRIAL SCIENTISTS ARE UNHAPPY

On a more objective plane, several attitude surveys have indicated that all is not well with professional employees in industry. For example, data on the University of Chicago's "Employee Inventory" were obtained from 587 engineers and natural scientists in 19 work groups. Most of the natural scientists were chemists and physicists, and a substantial number of them were Ph.D's.

The attitudes of the professional people included in this survey were found to be only slightly higher than those of factory labor or production workers surveyed by means of the "Employee Inventory" in other studies. The scientists and engineers were definitely less satisfied than management personnel, salesmen, foremen, or skilled workers; actually, in terms of this survey, their feelings appeared to be about the same as those of routine office employees. In almost all of the professional groups there was strong evidence of generalized dissatisfaction and frustration.

Other studies have reported similar findings and have identified considerable dissatisfaction and a wide gulf between the attitudes and expectations of scientists and engineers on the one hand and those of management on the other. The scientist generally sees his role as one of pushing back the frontiers of knowledge. To him, management's concern with profits and its immediate needs for new gimmicks and products to meet competition are little more than "bourgeois commercialism." The fact that he must submit to these commercial pressures is viewed as a source of considerable frustration.

In the face of all the frustration and commercial pressures of industry, why doesn't the scientist stay in the university? Three reasons have been cited:

1. They need the facilities, equipment, and project opportunities that they cannot find seemingly in the university.
2. They need the stimulation of colleagues active in the same or allied fields.
3. They desire or need the somewhat larger salaries obtainable in industry in comparison with those typical in academic institutions.

Thus the attitude survey data and general commentaries on the state of industrial research tend to leave us with a picture of the creative scientists being forced into industry as a matter of practicality and being miserable with his lot, his creative potential chafing against the chains of organizational control and nearsighted management.

PROPOSED CORRECTIVE ACTION

The array of remedies and cures for the problems of industrial research productivity read like the table of contents to a book on industrial management. A few illustrative examples are as follows.

1. *Improve the effectiveness of research management.* It has been suggested that the "gulf of mutual incomprehension" between scientists and managers is largely a management problem of balancing off technical versus administrative roles. At least one writer feels that this gulf can be bridged by looking ahead, crystalizing business goals, and clarifying research goals. In other words, more direct attention to the problems of research management should serve to increase research productivity.

2. *Provide better leadership in the laboratory.* Research studies have investigated the patterns of leadership utilized by managers of research laboratories and the impact of the leader on the satisfactions, motivations, and sense of progress of research scientists. These studies have generally concluded that:

a. When the laboratory chief is highly competent and has high scientific motivation, a participatory leadership pattern is most effective in building motivation and a sense of progress toward laboratory goals on the part of laboratory scientists. Participatory leadership is also most effective in building favorable attitudes toward the leader.

b. A chief of low competence and scientific motivation is better off with a laissez faire leadership pattern, though this will do little to build motivation and a sense of progress in the group.

c. Under all circumstances, a pattern of directive leadership is the least effective in a research organization.

3. *Reorganize the research function.* Many commentators feel that a

major reorganization of the research function is necessary and that basic research in industry should be separated both physically and budgetarily from product development. The primary objective of this proposed reorganization should be to create an atmosphere similar to that found in universities where most basic research is done. It is emphasized that every effort should be made to remove organizational controls to allow the full exercise of creativity.

4. *Provide improved compensation and recognition.* It has been pointed out that a sound management policy toward professional workers must provide that they be treated as members of the management team as well as members of their profession. To this end, they should be compensated at a level clearly above that of nonprofessional employees, should receive appropriate recognition both for work accomplished and for their professional status, be encouraged to participate actively in the appropriate professional societies, and be allowed to participate in decision making and other managerial processes.

The adoption by many companies of salary administration schemes employing the so-called dual ladder of promotion, status, and pay is a direct result of this concern. As is frequently the case with new personnel techniques, the decision to adopt these schemes seems to be based more often on a "get on the bandwagon" attitude than on a careful evaluation of organizational needs. In view of the small amount of effort devoted to nurturing and sustaining many of these programs, it is little wonder that they frequently fail to produce the expected results. In some instances, the technical ladder has actually come to serve as a convenient dumping ground for ineffective supervisory personnel.

5. *Utilize available scientific and technical talent more effectively.* Many writers blame the current supposed shortage of scientists and engineers on poor utilization of available talent. Attitude surveys of professional employees often show that the employees themselves are dissatisfied with the extent to which their skills and abilities are being used. There is, however, very little objective evidence to indicate how effectively or ineffectively technical talent is presently being utilized, or in what areas improvements can be made.

6. *Remove Governmental influence.* A number of strains between science and Government which tend to promote applied research and development at the expense of basic research have been noted. Since more than half of the total national expenditure for scientific research and development today is made by the Federal Government, the strains between the value systems of science and Government directly affect the nation's research productivity.

Other commentators have deplored the extent to which Government sponsorship of research breeds "projectitis"—the preplanned study with a precisely specified goal, passed on by an advisory board or a committee. Although "projectitis" occurs in industry, it is particularly prevalent where Government has a role in financing research. The necessity for detailed outlining of research procedures in applications for grants does considerable damage:

- The requirement to give precise indications of probable results tends to encourage deception.
- Sometimes unnecessary equipment is obtained in order to use up project funds.
- Research workers tend to be reduced to the status of technicians.
- Research effort is reduced to the common denominator of the committee's views and beliefs.
- The "puzzlement" which has led to many significant discoveries is discouraged.

7. *Import the academic climate.* When most of the proposed remedies to the problems of industrial scientific research are boiled down, they seem to say that the solution lies in making the atmosphere of industrial research laboratories as much as possible like that of the university. The sequence of logic in arriving at this conclusion is clear:

- Scientists are different. They want to create; they have the potentiality for creativity by virtue of the very fact that they are scientists.
- This potentiality for creativity is inhibited by bureaucratic structure. Archaic production-oriented organization and management, plus a lack of recognition of the fact that scientists are different, dams up the flow of creativity in industry.
- Yet industry is aware that it must have creativity in order to prosper and perhaps even to survive.
- Scientists in the academic environment are creative: most basic research is done in universities.
- The obvious solution, therefore, is to release the flow of creativity by removing the bureaucratic restraints and copying the conditions of the academic "idea factory."

This conclusion leads then to the specific conditions which are to be copied from the universities: organizational and administrative patterns which give the scientist the freedom to do what he wants, recognition for professional accomplishment, encouragement of publication, avoidance of anything smacking of commercialism or practicality; plus a high salary, good equipment, and adequate staff assistance. As is likely to be true of any position which has as many advocates as this, it undoubtedly has some validity in part—at least in its underlying logic. Academic scientists do, on the whole, accomplish more basic scientific research than do industrial scientists. Bureaucratic structure does, admittedly, present certain conflicts and barriers to creative scientific research. And there are, probably, scientists in industry who really want to be creative and who have the potentiality of making major scientific discoveries. As we have observed, however, there are a number of unknowns which tend to be ignored in arriving at this easy solution.

FOUR SOURCES OF BIAS

Throughout most of these exhortations to industry there runs a considerable amount of overgeneralization. Four main sources of bias are especially prevalent. Thus, it is widely assumed that (1) industry universally needs creativity; (2) the faults and failures of American scientific research are primarily found in the industrial environment; (3) the scientist-engineer is a distinct and well-defined human subtype, with clear-cut (if different) implications for management; and (4) creativity is a clearly defined and understood psychological construct or trait.

WHAT INDUSTRY NEEDS

It is quite generally assumed among the popular diagnosticians of the industrial research dilemma that what industry needs and wants in its scientific research efforts is a high order of original creative thinking. All scientific research tends to be regarded as creative in nature; and since industry engages in scientific research, it obviously follows that all industrial research requires a high level of creativity.

The fact of the matter is that most of the activity in which industrial laboratories engage does not, by its nature, require a high level of originality or creativity. Actually, as one might reasonably suppose, the greater part of industrial scientific activity consists of relatively routine testing and applications. This is of course as it should be, for it is in this bread-and-butter effort that science makes its most direct and consistent contribution to the industrial enterprise. In the current concern for creativity, however, this essential and primary function of industrial scientific research tends to be given a low priority.

INDUSTRY THE SCAPEGOAT

Most of the recommendations for increasing scientific productivity are pointed directly and deliberately at industrial research laboratories. Implicitly, and sometimes quite explicitly, academic research is held up as the model. Although there have been a few published articles dealing with university research, most studies of the research process have been conducted in industry. Under these circumstances, there is little wonder that all of the faults and failures of the American scientific research effort have been found in industry.

In the face of this constant bombardment, the best defense that industry can muster, apparently, is an occasional feeble rejoinder to the effect that increased support for basic research takes time. Industry never questions that this is what it should and must do, and it seldom takes pot shots at the vulnerable areas in the academic model which is held up to it. Yet some pot shots might well be in order.

In addition, this emphasis on specific practices within industry tends to overlook an examination of general factors in our culture which are vital in considerations of scientific productivity. To the extent that there are problems, the causes can at least in part be traced to the general structure and values of our contemporary society.

THE SCIENTIST STEREOTYPE

Because industry hires a vast number of people with Ph.D's in science and engineering to staff its research laboratories, it is generally assumed that industry has on hand an ample supply of creative potential. It is only because of inefficient utilization and ineffective management that its productivity is not as high as it might be. After all, the reasoning goes, a scientist is a scientist, and all scientists want the same thing: to push back the frontiers of knowledge. And a man must certainly be capable of high-level scientific research if he is able to get a Ph.D. in science. So industry obviously must be at fault for putting roadblocks in the path of these dedicated and capable people.

The almost universal tendency to lump scientists and engineers into a single category when discussing research management provides an indication of the extent to which the scientist stereotype prevails The fact is, as common sense suggests, that in general there are important differences with regard to job content, training, professional identification, aspiration, and the like between scientists and engineers. Research has shown that marked differences exist among the various scientific disciplines, and the differences between scientists and engineers are especially notable.

THE CREATIVE STEREOTYPE

The use of the word "creative" in connection with science and scientists has generated another stereotype which is almost universally accepted by the general public and all too frequently by scholars and research administrators as well. This stereotype is closely related to the "scientist" stereotype. We tend to regard a creative act in science as one that results in a major breakthrough—the theory of relativity, for example, or the development of the transistor. Creativity, in this view, is the process behind some marvelous new invention. We look qualitatively at the results of an activity; and if they exceed a certain standard of utility and newness, we call the activity a "creative" one.

However, this method of designating an act as creative if it leads to something new and useful does little to enhance our understanding of creativity. If two people independently arrive at the same original idea, is the first to do so creative and the second not creative simply because the result is no longer new? And if an activity is regarded as not creative if its results have no present utility, what happens if at some time in the future it is found to be useful? Does the previous act of evolving the idea then change from a noncreative to a creative act? And who is to determine how useful the results of an activity must be in order for the activity to be creative? Unfortunately creativity conceived of in terms of the newness, utility, or magnitude of results will lead us only into a semantic swamp and give no sound basis for identifying a given act as creative.

On the other hand, attempts to remove the elements of utility and novelty from the definition of creativity lead to shallow concepts which lose the flavor of creativity as something rare and awe inspiring. For example, a reasonable working definition which has been used to designate an act as creative or not creative states that to create means "to recombine existing elements or facts in ways which are new as far as the creator is concerned." This definition realistically emphasizes that a creation is merely a recombining of existing elements (parts, molecules, words, colors, concepts, and so on) in ways which are new to the person who is creating. To many, however, such a definition will undoubtedly be unacceptable as it doesn't agree with their preconceptions.

In any event, the words "creative" and "creativity" continue to be used in writing about research productivity and administration as though they represented a well-defined and thoroughly understood psychological construct. As we shall see, this assumption is far from justified.

CURRENT THEORY AND KNOWLEDGE ABOUT CREATIVITY

Like efforts to define creativity or to identify a creative act, attempts to evaluate the on-going phenomenon of creativity frequently lead to confusion and too narrow an interpretation of the domain of the creative process. Studies of the phenomenon of creativity tend to focus on one of two aspects: (1) the psychological processes within the individual associated with a creative act or (2) the environmental and social correlates of creativity. The aspect chosen generally reflects the secular interests of the investigator, and there has been little if any research effort which systematically covers both aspects of the subject. Some research has been done which deals with these two aspects of creativity.

CREATIVITY AS AN INDIVIDUAL PSYCHOLOGICAL PHENOMENON

In considering creativity as an individual phenomenon, many psychologists have concentrated on the development of tests which demonstrate a statistical relationship to measures of creative performance. In some cases, inferences about creativity have been drawn from the statistical interrelationship of the scores on tests designed to measure psychological dimensions hypothesized to be important factors in creativity. Other psychologists have emphasized study of the creative personality and have attempted to identify specific traits which are characteristic of highly creative people. Still others have attempted to identify and describe the various stages of mental activity involved in the on-going creative act.

The tests and measurements approach. Perhaps the most extensive research in developing tests of creative ability has been conducted by J. P. Guilford and his associates at the University of Southern California under contract with the Office of Naval Research. This research has consisted largely of statistical studies of mental abilities and has employed factor-analytic techniques. Guilford hypothesized a number of creativity factors dealing with primary abilities, to which he has given such names as:

1. Sensitivity to problems.
2. Ideational fluency.
3. Flexibility of set.
4. Ideational novelty.
5. Synthesizing ability.
6. Analyzing ability.
7. Reorganizing or redefining ability.
8. Span of ideational structure.
9. Evaluating ability.

It was recognized that in different fields, different patterns of primary abilities would undoubtedly be related to creative ability.

Guilford's approach has been to develop a large battery of tests designed to measure the hypothesized creative ability factors. These tests are then given to a group of subjects (in his studies these have usually been air cadets or OCS students). The interrelationships among the test scores are statistically analyzed, and the extent to which specific tests co-vary or cluster is evaluated. Statistical clustering or interrelationships of test scores indicate that the tests are measuring common components of mental ability, or factors; and the nature of the factor is being measured is identified from the tests which cluster together or "load" on it. If similar factors are obtained in repeated studies using different varieties of tests, the tests are held to be valid measures of the construct under consideration.

Guilford and his associates have had considerable success in isolating factors of creative ability in a number of groups which have been tested. This success should not be too surprising, since Guilford constructed his tests to measure hypothesized factors in mental ability. Thus, he has essentially gotten out of his analysis what he put into it. His analysis has also served, however, to identify additional factors and to clarify the nature of the test battery. As result of this and other factor-analytic studies, Guilford feels that it is possible to measure individual differences in originality or creativity through the use of psychological tests.

Attempts to transfer Guilford's tests from the laboratory to the industrial setting, however, and to relate them to external measures of creativity, or criteria, have not been resoundingly successful—although the results show promise and certainly suggest that additional effort in this area is warranted. One of the primary difficulties is the old and familiar criterion problem, the psychologist's nemesis. In the absence of an objective measure of creativity, validation studies must resort to subjective evaluations or ratings. Ratings of creativity or originality are, no doubt, even less reliable than ratings of production since, as we noted earlier, there seems to be only a very inexact notion of just what creativity is. Some studies try to get around the rating problem by using the number of publications or patents which a researcher has as a criterion. However, the relationship of this criterion to the psychological correlates of creativity is tenuous.

Guilford's success in building a creativity construct may be assessed to some extent by the number of studies which use scores on various of his tests themselves as a criterion of creativity—a questionable practice at best. The extent to which this practice is resorted to also serves to indicate how difficult it is to develop a suitable external measure of creativity.

Although the tests and measurements approach holds promise of making important contributions to management's efforts to identify creative talent for industrial research, it is evident that considerable refinement of the techniques is required. Most of this refinement will have to be done in the industrial setting. If the ultimate objective is to predict what might be called "operational creativity"—that is, scientific performance as it is important for particular purposes in specific industrial settings—research to date provides a good foundation on which to build. Studies within industry can be tailored to each specific situation and to the appropriate criteria of creativity (which probably differ from one situation to another). When research is tailored to each specific situation, the prospects for positive results are excellent. As results are accumulated in various operational settings, it may be possible to assimilate them into more general formulations about the nature of creative ability. But the possibility of creativity testing payout now rests largely with management, and carefully conceived studies within specific settings are needed.

The creative personality. It is a somewhat artificial distinction to consider research studies of the creative personality separately from the tests and measurements approach. It is clear that objective psychological tests (such as those developed by Guilford to measure factors of creative ability) provide important insights for describing the creative personality. However, most research in this area relies heavily on "projective" personality test data and on extensive interviews by psychologists. Also, some of the most interesting writings about the creative personality are more anecdotal than statistical. For the sake of clarity, the results of these researches are discussed separately here.

One fact has become quite clear as a result of numerous research studies: there is no such thing as *the* creative personality. It is misleading to assume that *all* highly creative people have some specific, identifiable personality make-up which distinguishes them from the general population. Although research has identified personality characteristics which appear more descriptive of creative people as a group than of the general population, there are always individual exceptions which do not fit the general pattern.

It is also misleading to assume that the personality pattern exhibited by most people who are highly creative in one field is necessarily the same pattern as that of most creative people in a different field. For example, although they have many characteristics in common, creative writers as a group tend to exhibit somewhat different personality patterns from creative mathematicians, who in turn tend to differ from creative architects.

Studies also suggest significant differences among different scientific disciplines, such as chemists versus physicists, physicists versus biologists, and so forth. These findings should serve as a caution to those who blithely recommend various techniques for dealing with scientists in general. And they should serve as even more of a caution against the practice of lumping scientists and engineers into a single category.

Several personality characteristics have been identified which appear to be characteristic of most creative people in all fields. First and foremost, highly creative people are dedicated to their work. They have a strong commitment to their goals and are generally highly self-confident in pursuing their objectives. They tend to be independent and nonconformists—intellectual nonconformists, though not necessarily social nonconformists. They value the freedom to set their own goals and to pursue them in their own way. In sum, they are intensely dedicated and self-reliant individuals.

In addition to a strong dedication to their work, highly creative people are intelligent. As a group they score well above average on standard intelligence tests. However, aside from a certain basic (and relatively high) level of intelligence, there is no significant relationship between intelligence and creativity. Thus, it is perfectly possible for a person to score extremely high on a standard intelligence test and still not be highly creative.

Highly creative people differ from the general population in terms of their patterns of interests. On standard vocational interest inventories, they tend to score low on scales for such occupations as office workers, farmers, or bankers. They all score high on scales for author-journalists, psychologists, or architects. We may infer that highly creative people tend to be most interested in concepts, in the meanings and implications of ideas or things, or in abstractions. They tend not to be interested in small detail or in fields which are predominately practical and concrete.

On tests designed to measure the extent to which an individual holds each of six basic human values—aesthetic, economic, political, social, religious, and theoretical—highly creative people tend to hold most strongly to the aesthetic and theoretical values. They score low in terms of economic values. Although aesthetic and theoretical values would generally be assumed to be conflicting, highly creative people in all categories appear able to resolve whatever conflict is entailed and hold both patterns of values with approximately equal strength. They are able to tolerate the inner tensions created by holding to these conflicting value systems.

Similarly, it has been pointed out that highly creative people seem able to tolerate ambiguity in a situation. Actually, they exhibit a preference for the complex when presented with a series of patterns or designs. They feel less compulsion to immediately impose order out of chaos than do less creative persons.

One striking finding is that highly creative people almost universally tend to perceive the world in terms of implications. They are overwhelm-

ingly intuitive and focus upon possibilities—the realm of "what could be."
On the other hand, roughly 75 per cent of the general population focus
their attention on facts—the realm of "what is"—as perceived by their
five senses. An approach to the world in which there is a continual search
for a link to new possibilities is an almost universal characteristic of
highly creative individuals.

In general it can be said that studies of the creative personality support
the idea that scientists are somehow different from the average industrial
employee and require different treatment. At least, highly creative scientists are different and are intensely dedicated to their work. But the
extent to which differences are peculiar to outstandingly creative scientists
is open to question; intense dedication (motivation) is undoubtedly related to outstanding performance in most fields. It would probably not
be overstepping the data, however, to conclude that a strong sense
of dedication is a necessary (though probably not sufficient) prerequisite
for sustained creative scientific performance. Thus it would appear justified for research administrators to employ whatever different handling
would serve to promote and sustain a high level of scientific dedication
among their research personnel.

It is difficult and may be dangerous, however, to suggest general principles or techniques for this different handling of scientific personnel. For
the research administrator, it implies manipulation of the industrial environment into which the research scientist is placed. Knowledge of the
relationships between environmental variables and creative performance
is sketchy at best. However, a common-sense analysis of the requirements
of scientific research can identify some of the variables. Also a limited
amount of social science research has identified other pertinent factors—
pertinent, at least, in the organizational settings in which the research was
carried on.

Phases of the creative process. A number of investigators have attempted
to define the various phases of the creative process. Generally, four basic
stages of creativity are identified:

1. Preparation: the subject's thoughts are changing rapidly and he
   is receiving new ideas.
2. Incubation: a single idea or concept recurs spontaneously from
   time to time with some modification occurring while the subject
   is thinking of other matters.
3. Illumination: the idea or concept is distinctly formulated.
4. Verification: the idea or concept is tested by research, experimen-
   tation, or other means.

Although the names given to the various stages may vary from one writer to the next, the processes involved are generally similar. In the General Electric Company's Creative Engineering Program, for example, the creative act is broken down as follows:

1. Definition of the problem.
2. Search for a method of solving the problem.
3. Period of thought resulting in inspiration.
4. Reduction of the idea to practice.

This clearly represents an attempt to put the classical breakdown of the creative process into a framework appropriate to the industrial research environment.

SOCIAL AND ENVIRONMENTAL CORRELATES OF CREATIVITY

It seems reasonable to suppose that if an individual scientist has the necessary mental capacity for creative thinking, the appropriate technical skills and knowledge, and perhaps the proper personality make-up as well, whether or not he is actually creative will probably depend largely on external environmental factors. First, and most obviously, the environment must provide an *opportunity* for the scientist to recognize and investigate pertinent problem areas, to gain initial problem sensitivity— the essential first ingredient of the creative process. The second vital element which the environment must provide is *reinforcement:* the availability of those environmental factors which tend to encourage and sustain the scientist in his creative effort. Research studies have suggested a number of areas in which such reinforcement factors may or may not be present, including organization structure, communication patterns, leadership (or the lack of it), and composition of the work team.

Opportunity to gain sensitivity. Obviously, creativity cannot occur in a vacuum. The individual must first of all be aware that a problem exists; he must be exposed to situations which challenge his creative capacity and demand solution. In science this calls for some knowledge of the technical field so that the problem will be recognized as a problem and so that appropriate methods of attacking it will be known.

It has been suggested, however, that the individual should not have too much knowledge of the field. One well-known research director has said that he prefers to hire relatively inexperienced researchers because they don't know so much that they are "sure" a particular line of attack "won't work." Although this position has probably been overstated, it does seem to have some validity. Several studies of groups of eminent creative people in many different fields have shown that they frequently make their most important contributions at an early age.

It may be that increased familiarity with a field tends to decrease an individual's sensitivity to problem areas. This leads to an overly fatalistic and gloomy picture of creativity, and it should be pointed out that a considerable amount of controversy has been generated over this issue. But these studies of the relationship between age and creativity do suggest the importance of providing problem sensitivity and encouragement early in a scientist's career.

Sensitivity to problems is also a function of the culture and the social environment in which the scientist grew up and in which he works. If the culture insists on conformity and adherence to established techniques and practices, there is little chance for creative innovation. To encourage sensitivity to problem areas, the culture must value, or at the very least tolerate, deviation from the status quo.

It is also clear that the attitude toward a particular area of research or investigation held by the society as a whole influences the likelihood of creative achievement in that area. Thus, for example, the present emphasis in the United States on biochemistry or on aero-space has been responsible for a tremendous increase in scientific research in these areas. Widespread interest in all sectors of our society—among the general public as well as in the scientific, business, Government, and military communities—serves to channel the attention of American scientists and to increase their sensitivity to problems requiring solution. To a considerable extent, increased research activity in these areas can be attributed to the enormous amounts of money which are being spent. But the importance of the interests and expectations of the general public must not be underestimated.

Reinforcement. Closely related to the environmental variables of opportunity to gain sensitivity to problem areas are a host of factors which might loosely be subsumed under the term "reinforcement." These are the factors with which most research administrators are concerned. They can be thought of as all of the environmental factors which tend to encourage and support creative research. They include leadership variables, organizational variables, and interpersonal variables. It is in these areas that most of the recommendations for improved research administration are made. And it is also in these areas that there is so much difference of opinion and so little that can be stated without qualification.

In considering some of these environmental variables we will take for granted the obvious: physical equipment. Without the reinforcement of the often complex equipment required for present-day scientific research, other environmental variables can have little effect.

A University of Michigan study carried out at the National Institutes of Health investigated, among other things, the relationship between supervision and research performance. The study found that frequent stimulation and encouragement from the supervisor contributed to high research performance. At the same time it was concluded that subordinates should be given considerable freedom to make their own decisions and to exercise their own initiative. Freedom for the researcher to carry out his work as he sees fit is generally regarded as a primary environmental variable and is at the core of most of the recommendations which have been made.

A certain amount of research into the nature of productive work groups has been done. The NIH study, for example, found a tendency for frequent contact with colleagues who have dissimilar values and dissimilar previous work experience to be related to high performance. These NIH findings fit in with a whole school of thought which advocates the use of research teams made up of scientists with heterogeneous backgrounds and values.

In the area of group research, an MIT study presented data which tend to repeal the "iron law" that creativity declines as age increases. The study suggested that lowering the average age of a research and development team tends to increase the creativity of the individual members of the team, regardless of their own chronological age. The data indicate even more strongly that young groups—that is, groups whose members have been working together for only a relatively short period of time—receive higher creativity ratings than do old groups. The obvious implication is for putting new blood on the R&D team from time to time.

A belief in the effectiveness of group factors in providing reinforcement for creativity forms the major platform for the school of thought which advocates group brainstorming. The brainstorming approach is based upon the notion that if you produce a large enough *quantity* of ideas, at least some ideas of good quality will be included. The rules of brainstorming state that after a problem to be solved has been formulated and expressed to the group, all ideas which come to mind should be expressed by the group members without any attempt to evaluate them. No one should stop to explore or find fault with any idea. Brainstormers are supposed to reach for and express any kind of idea, no matter how remote it may seem at the time; ideas should be evaluated and the wheat separated from the chaff after the brainstorming session has run its course. Theoretically, the group helps increase the flow of ideas.

Research indicates that the basic brainstorming approach may have some merit. It has been shown that brainstorming experience can increase the scores of participants on some of the creativity tests developed by J. P. Guilford, as measured in terms of both quantity of ideas and quality of ideas. Another study has shown that significantly more ideas rated as "good" were produced under typical brainstorming instructions (emphasizing that no evaluation of the ideas was to be made) than under non-brainstorming instructions (in which only "good" ideas were sought). Although the basic idea of deferring evaluation of ideas is probably helpful, there is some doubt about the value of group reinforcement in brainstorming. Several studies have compared the productivity of groups of people working together under brainstorming instructions with the productivity of a similar number of people working alone under brainstorming rules. In these studies, individuals working alone, when their responses were totaled, collectively produced a greater mean total number of ideas, a greater mean number of unique ideas, and ideas of higher quality. Under brainstorming rules, group influences may actually inhibit getting full benefit from the technique.

Some studies dealing with the research environment have investigated the patterns of motivation of scientific personnel. Two motivational patterns are usually delineated: the science orientation and the institutional orientation. The NIH study, for example, found that high research performance was generally associated with high science orientation. However, performance in research was not so high when the individual exhibited both strong science motivation and strong institutional motivation. It was hypothesized that under these conditions there is a conflict between goals for the individual and that his scientific performance declines to the extent that he devotes energy toward his institutional orientation. Attitude survey results frequently tend to support this interpretation.

There have been other studies dealing with the research environment which purport to identify variables associated with creativity. As is true even of the few results reported here, the data require a certain amount of stretching to see a direct tie to scientific creativity in a general sense—that is to say, beyond the particular situation in which they were collected. Perhaps the safest statement one can make is that we really know very little about the effects of environment on creative performance. The studies provide fuel for speculation and for the generation of hypotheses, but very little direct data. Recommendations based on these studies should be taken in this light; however, they are seldom *given* in this light.

IMPLICATIONS FOR INDUSTRIAL RESEARCH MANAGERS

There is today a veritable flood of written commentary on the subject of creativity in scientific research and particularly in industrial scientific research. Most of this commentary must be based upon common sense, speculation, or clairvoyance, because very little is conclusively known about creativity.

Industrial managers, however, cannot wait and should not be expected to wait for conclusive, generalizable research findings on creativity for use in their organizations. Research to date has, at the very least, served to emphasize how much we do *not* know, and in the process it has helped to focus our attention on those areas which are most important. From this identification of problem areas, it is possible to derive informed judgments and tentative conclusions.

IMPLICATIONS FOR SELECTION

For the individual company interested in the possibility of enhancing the creativity of its research personnel, there is a very good chance that well-designed programs of selection and placement can be of significant help. Present testing programs cannot be universally applied, but they show promise. It should be possible to adapt and expand them to fit a variety of situations. Efforts to predict success must be tailored to each individual research situation and also to the different kinds of people being considered. More careful attention to the definition and measurement of success—that is, to the *criteria* of success, which can be expected to vary from one situation to another—is essential and should lead to more conclusive results for the organization. In a sense, industry has a responsibility to extend the considerable results of laboratory studies and to accumulate data within specific operating situations. Such data may then help to clarify and expand the more general formulations dealing with creative mental abilities.

PROMOTING PROBLEM SENSITIVITY

Management should constantly strive to promote sensitivity to problems and alternative approaches on the part of its research personnel. This includes encouragement to keep abreast of the technical literature and encouraging interaction with professional colleagues through such means as attendance at meetings of professional societies. Interaction with other members of the organization—people in engineering, production, sales, and so forth—might also help to broaden the thinking of research personnel, and to increase their sensitivity to problem areas and approaches; and they should perhaps be encouraged on an informal basis.

We should recognize that problem sensitivity may become an increasingly important consideration as the age of the industrial research population increases. Whether the iron law of creativity operates or not may be subject to debate, but there is little doubt that the substantive content of science is increasing at a fantastic rate and that technical skills and knowledge can quickly become obsolete. The prevention of technological obsolescence within the organization is a vital responsibility of management and an essential ingredient of any effort to enhance creativity.

Research teams and groups may in some situations help to promote sensitivity. Diversity of backgrounds and interests among group members may stimulate fresh viewpoints and approaches. Group composition should probably be flexible, with an occasional infusion of new members. Adequate communication networks within and among groups must be provided for. The team approach in research should not be blindly and inflexibly adopted; rather, its use should depend on the nature of the project under consideration and the preferences of the individuals involved. A group is not creative, per se, but group interaction may enhance creativity of the members.

The decision to segregate the research function organizationally and physically should be carefully weighed. Although such segregation is widely advocated, it is possible that valuable interaction and problem sensitivity can be lost through the isolation of research personnel. Certainly an argument can be made for segregating that type of research which is variously termed "pure" or "fundamental" or "basic," but the line of demarcation between such effort and "applied" research or "development" is hazy and the argument inconclusive. In all of these matters, management will have to play it by ear according to its individual situation and requirements. The functional as well as the dysfunctional aspects of research segregation should be recognized and weighed.

"Projectitis"—the overly detailed outlining of research objectives and procedures—should be avoided whenever possible. The premature and too extensive delineation of project details can serve only to stifle creativity and reduce research to a cookbook application. The development of sensitivity to alternative approaches and ramifications is precluded by project outlines which are excessively rigid. Certainly advance planning is necessary, but it should be as general and flexible as possible; and it should be participated in, to the greatest possible extent, by those who will ultimately do the work.

THE LEADERSHIP ROLE OF THE RESEARCH SUPERVISOR

As in most things, the direct approach is probably the most effective in efforts to enhance the creativity of industrial researchers. Research managers should probably devote most of their attention to those variables which provide reinforcement and encouragement for creative performance within the organization. However, this attention should *not* take the form of making a fetish of the creative stereotype.

It goes without saying that achieving optimum utilization of the talents, training, and interests of the workforce is a prime management responsibility. Underutilizing high-caliber personnel is the surest way of dampening what is unquestionably the most important single ingredient of creativity: motivation. It is also quite expensive.

It can probably be said that within an industrial organizational setting the most effective reinforcement for outstanding research performance flows from people rather than from things. Things (a fancy title, private parking space, and—to a degree—salary) serve largely as symbols which are motivationally effective to the extent that they represent the approbation of people. In research, the approval and recognition of the scientific community is often a critical motivational factor, but the "official" approval of one's superiors is also important. Thus, the most clear-cut locus for approbation and reinforcement, in an organizational sense, is with the researcher's immediate superior—the research supervisor or leader. The first-line supervisor plays a vital role in all organizations, but probably nowhere more so than in the research organization. For it is only through the first-line supervisor that management can approach and deal with the highly individual problems—and products—of the creative research man.

There are, it seems, two basic attributes of the ideal research supervisor which are rarely found in a single individual: (1) he must be technically competent, if not outstanding, and (2) he must have an understanding of human nature and empathy for the problems of the individuals whom he supervises. Technical competence is necessary, not so much for the actual direction of research effort but for insuring the leader's acceptance as a worthwhile and desired source of approval and reinforcement by his people.

The use of high-caliber technical talent in a supervisory role should not be viewed by management as a symptom of poor utilization. It becomes poor utilization only when and to the extent that the technical supervisor is burdened with nontechnical responsibilities and details. It is also poor utilization when and to the extent that the supervisory role is viewed as a burden by the individual to whom it is assigned—which brings us, of course, to the second necessary attribute of the ideal research supervisor.

The role of the leader as a source of reinforcement and encouragement calls for considerable skill in understanding the motivations and behavior of the group members. A participatory pattern of leadership should be developed—an atmosphere of working *with* rather than *for* the leader. The vague abstraction, "research freedom," which is so much talked about, can be traced most meaningfully to the relationship between leader and group member. The importance of freedom in the sense of the absence of bureaucratic rules and restraints (as manifested, for example, in flexible working hours, few report forms to be filled out, and a minimum of red tape) is insignificant along side this relationship. Effective reinforcement for research performance requires of the leader a desire to fulfill the reinforcing role, as well as skills and understanding in dealing with people. Such skill and understanding can, and probably should, be developed through research-leadership training programs specifically designed for that purpose, but the desire to fulfill the reinforcing role is beyond the reach of training and should be a vital consideration in the selection of supervisory personnel.

For the supervisor, the value of participative leadership in research exceeds the single purpose of providing reinforcement. It fosters problem sensitivity by increasing interaction within and among research groups. It encourages individual attention to all group members—newcomers as well as old-timers. (This may be particularly important in research in view of the possible inverse age-creativity relationship and the rapid obsolescence of skills.)

RECOGNIZING INDIVIDUAL VARIATIONS

One conclusion runs consistently through all the rest: research managers must recognize and provide for individual differences among their people. Variations, sometimes extreme, in personality, ability, and interest must be accommodated. Nonconformity (in a social sense) should be tolerated *if* it is a genuine aspect of the behavior and personality pattern of a highly productive individual. Conscious bohemianism can be disruptive and is usually unrelated to performance.

Management should recognize that dissatisfaction or low morale—as evidenced by attitude surveys and other measures—may not be a bad thing per se. A positive relationship between morale and productivity has not been conclusively demonstrated even among blue collar and clerical personnel. It is quite possible, though it has not been proved, that dissatisfaction with the status quo may be positively related to research performance. Of course, the evaluation of survey results depends directly on what the data reveal as elements of dissatisfaction. Frequently, factors which represent real and direct barriers to research productivity are identified in this manner. Such barriers clearly should be corrected.

Genuine dissatisfaction with minor and peripheral elements of the environment (the cafeteria, parking facilities, and the like) may lead to misdirection of attention and unnecessary frustration, but it is usually quite difficult to determine whether such dissatisfaction is genuine or a reflection of general (and possibly functional) dissatisfaction with the status quo. To the extent possible, dissatisfaction should be focused toward technical problems and their solution.

As a general rule, the primary orientation of research personnel should be toward the scientific community rather than toward the institution. But the facts of business life make total attainment of this objective impossible. Industrial research scientists are probably more aware of this than most observers realize. Exhortations to industry to emulate the academic environment and import the graduate school atmosphere are essentially meaningless abstractions; the university *cannot* be duplicated in industry.

GUIDELINES FOR SUPERVISING RESEARCH •

JULES D. PORSCHE

TALKING AND WRITING ABOUT creativity and creative thinking seem to have become fads among managers, particularly research managers. It does seem odd that those who have been vitally involved in research for many years have only recently become interested in research on research, or research which will permit them to understand more completely the creative activity which occurs in their organizations.

Some discussions reveal a considerable reverence toward creative ability. This is unfortunate. We must remember that the creative mind is only one of the many requirements in industry. Those concerned with research may be inclined to the misconception that the research department has a monopoly on it. This is far from true. Numerous ideas for new products and new processes originate outside of research. Creative ability is a powerful asset to a corporate executive in many phases of his work. Sales and merchandising activities are constantly seeking new concepts, new techniques. Perhaps production is the stiffest leg in the familiar three-legged stool, inasmuch as products must be manufactured which do not vary in quality. But, even within the rigid framework of the flow sheet, there is opportunity for the creative mind to devise improvements or reduce costs in accepted processes. The same is true of the various service activities in a corporation. Opportunities for developing new and novel approaches to handling old problems are innumerable.

CREATIVE ABILITY DEFINED

What is creative ability? It is the faculty possessed by human beings for integrating into a new form the facts, impressions, or feelings which result

---

JULES D. PORSCHE is President, Jules D. Porsche and Associates, Clarendon Hills, Illinois.

from experience. It is the ability to establish new connections between facts or symbols. It is a capacity for gaining new insight into the relations between bits of existing knowledge. The result of creative effort may be a work of art, such as a painting or musical composition; it may be a new machine or a new product to be manufactured and sold; or it may be a new concept in philosophy or science. The creative person perceives the possibility of combining the products of his own intellectual or emotional experiences into something new. He feels impelled to do this. The actual process occurs during or after a period of incubation at the subconscious levels of the mind.

In many respects, this first phase of creative thinking resembles a dream. Certainly our dreams develop entirely new and often startling combinations of facts, and frequently do so in a quite artistic manner. All of us have had the experience of awakening from a sound sleep with the solution to a baffling problem. Literature is replete with examples of highly creative people who describe their more creative acts in association with the effects of alcohol, drugs, or reveries inspired by other means.

After this unordered or illogical creative process of integrating impressions, facts, and feelings into new structures, the logical, rational, and intellectual faculties take over and critically examine this creation. Is the new structure beautiful or useful? Will it be accepted? Will it add to the prestige of its creator? Is it so different that it will cause amusement?

The result of this creative activity must be either acceptable or tenable at the time the creative act is performed or at some time thereafter. Those who determine whether an act is creative are the critics, in the case of art; scientific colleagues, in the case of new scientific discoveries; and management, customers, and stockholders in the case of industry.

QUANTITATIVE VARIATIONS

I like to think of creative ability as a characteristic of all human beings, which varies quantitatively as well as qualitatively. It is this quantitative variation which enables some gifted individuals to conceive ideas much greater in scope than those of others.

The more creative scientists in industrial research, it has been found, are self-sufficient, self-reliant, self-confident. They work at a high energy level. They are career-oriented. They identify strongly with their companies.

Others, equally supplied with intelligence and training, experience difficulty with the free-wheeling stage of creative thinking. They cannot release the mental or emotional brakes and permit complete freedom of association. Often they apply logic and critical judgment too early, with the result that creative developments are suppressed at the embryonic stage. Such scientists often do their best in creating within the rigidly logical framework of scientific theory or in finding applications for the radical ideas of others. They prefer to use a deductive or theoretical approach to solve problems.

Still others show skill in just one phase of the creative process. Some are idea producers. Many will prefer to start with ideas of others, modifying and improving them. A few are skillful in persuading critics to accept and use new developments.

FACTORS IN MOTIVATION

What makes people do creative work? In order to have some understanding of the motivations behind creative activity, we need to consider both the individual and the environment in which he operates.

Studies indicate that in industrial chemical research the scientists are characterized by a very high level of intelligence. Indeed, they are in the upper 2 per cent of the population when classified according to IQ. However, although a high IQ may be necessary for a high order of creative ability, it does not insure it. There are some emotional factors involved in addition to intelligence. Moreover, the culture and the environment in which the individual does creative work are exceedingly important factors.

Although he may hide in his laboratory, a creative scientist has a strong need to assert himself and be independent. This may appear as a desire to publish papers and thereby gain prestige in the eyes of scientific colleagues. It may appear as a desire for recognition in the form of a title, a private office, two telephones, a secretary, and so on—or it may appear as a desire for financial remuneration. Combinations of two or more of these characteristics are not unknown among creative people, nor are they limited to creative people.

The creative person is a restless type of individual with certain unsatisfied emotional needs. We never see the complacent, self-satisfied individual coming up with a new and revolutionary idea. Somehow, the creative person sufferes from a certain degree of frustration which is satisfied by the familiar "Eureka!" which follows the gaining of new insight into a problem or the development of a new idea. Here we can go back to our dream analogy. It would appear that in order to induce creative thinking, one must generate a conflict. There must be an unsatisfied need. Perhaps it is a need for approval, prestige, or satisfaction of curiosity; a need to belong; or simply a need to create a new idea or concept. Just as our dreams show a way to combine available data into a form which will satisfy a need, so too does the successful creative act remove the frustration which results from the unsatisfied need for insight into a problem.

The compelling force or urgency which drives the creative worker must not be confused with anxiety or fear. It produces a positive or an offensive attitude in contrast to the defensive attitude characteristic of the anxious or fearful person. This defensive attitude is incompatible with effective creative work.

THE FRAMEWORK OF THOUGHT

Assuming we have a creative individual who is to develop new products, we must provide the environment in which he can perform effectively. A most important function of the environment is to provide the policy framework within which the creative mind must function. The aims and objectives of corporations and, therefore, of their research organizations must be spelled out so that creative individuals in the organization may be aware of the horizons within which they can operate. As a result of such a formulation of policy, one or more of three situations may stimulate a search for new products:

1. A recognized need exists for a new or improved product.
2. A material is available in quantity and low in cost.
3. An opportunity is available for original thinking with only the broadest of limitations as to product or use.

Recognized need. Perhaps the commonest reason for new product development is the desire to excel competitors. The commonest approach is the development of a new or improved product to fill an established need. The creative mind needs much factual information for its associations. For example, an analysis of existing products will reveal a number of advantages and a number of disadvantages. A study of the reactions of consumers will provide illuminating clues. In addition, a background of practical and theoretical knowledge is necessary to provide the rest of the material to be fed into the creative mental hopper.

Next, a period of incubation must take place, leading to the imaginative integration of these bits of knowledge and impressions into a new product idea. This new idea is then subjected to critical evaluation by the originator and others. It may be utilized as such, or it may be the source of inspiration to someone else who will modify it and improve it. This is the kind of thinking which led to such products as vacuum-packed meats, modern gasolines and lubricating products, and many new chemicals and plastics.

Available material. A similar analytical approach is helpful in starting one's thinking with a raw material. What are the physical and chemical properties of the material? Where does one need such physical and chemical properties? How could the material be transformed?

Opportunity for thinking. The third method requires a much less rigid or analytical approach. It does require the unhampered satisfaction of curiosity. Examples are found in the work of Irving Langmuir of General Electric and Wallace Carothers of Du Pont. The payoff from this freest kind of research is often the greatest, but the program requires long-term financial backing. Perhaps even more important, it thrives on the patient encouragement not often obtainable from the harried executive sorely pressed for immediate profit.

THE CRITIC'S ROLE

Just as the objectives of the corporation are of great importance in setting the framework of thought, the critics are very powerful factors in determining the scope of the creative person. In industrial research, many critics influence the creativity of the scientist: the man at the next bench, the supervisors, the research directors, and the officers and stockholders of the corporation. The research worker's composite view of the attitude of these critics plays an important role in determining the scope of his creative thinking. If it does not, the result can only be frustration.

A company with a good profit record, generous amounts of available capital, and a management oriented toward diversification is likely to stimulate the maximum of creative thought, not only in its research organization but throughout the rest of the company. This type of situation is conducive to a general feeling of confidence in the company and in many of the responsible individuals of the company, including one's self. It is accompanied by an atmosphere of acceptance of new ideas and new points of view. There need be no fear of expressing these ideas. New ideas are not considered as threatening or as criticism by those who might be involved in changes called for by these new ideas.

An environment of this kind tends to produce a snowballing effect. One is reminded of the old saying that "success breeds success." The entire atmosphere is one of urgency and tension. Financial rewards are good. Opportunities for personal growth and advancement are relatively numerous. Self-confidence and self-assertiveness are stimulated; and pride, if not conceit, is justified. Mutual stimulation of the individuals in the organization is automatic.

Consider, on the other hand, an idea in a company which is losing money. Fear is the dominant emotion—fear of criticism, fear of reduced income, or worse. Under these circumstances, any new idea or innovation is examined very critically from an entirely different point of view. The criterion employed by the critics is no longer "Will it make money?" but "How much will it cost? Will it save money?" When companies lose money, it is rare to find a board of directors willing to face the ire of the stockholders by deficit-financing facilities to manufacture a new product. The corporate objective becomes expense slashing and money saving.

What are the repercussions of these attitudes on the part of the critics? The creative individuals feel that their security is threatened by possible reductions in budget and a critical attitude, born of anxiety, which is adopted by the management toward the research activity and even toward science itself. The actual or potential reductions in budget mean the likelihood of less frequent raises and decreased opportunities for advancement. The net result is a sizable restriction in the horizons of thought, with a curtailment in scope, if not in frequency, of creative thinking.

ENTHUSIASTIC ACCEPTANCE

Once the framework within which the creative effort is to take place has been built, the environment must provide acceptance—preferably enthusiastic acceptance—of something really novel or new. This acceptance can best be provided by line supervisors of the research scientist, although acceptance by colleagues is highly important. Indeed, fellow scientists in the laboratory are among the more important critics who determine the direction and scope of the efforts of the creative individual. They are the mirrors used to reflect the impact of new hypotheses. They are the devil's advocates who can ferret out the weak spots in a new approach or an experimental design and perform this function in a positive and accepting manner. The importance of positive attitudes all around is immediately apparent.

Characteristic of the environment which has a markedly dampening effect on creative thought is secrecy. Within a company, a barrier to the communication of both information and ideas can be a very serious obstacle to the effective creative activity of individuals and particularly groups. Secrecy usually results from unhealthy competition among individuals or groups. It is unlikely to be a serious problem when the environment provides individuals with a feeling of security.

Charles F. Kettering, the great creative genius, awakened frequently in the middle of the night with ideas. It was his custom to record these ideas on the wallpaper close to his bed and then return to his slumbers. Such procedures would be frowned on in some homes where deviations from neat, orderly, standard practice are not tolerated. Even the home environment, however, must permit deviations from orderly procedures to encourage the development of creative ability. Similarly, the research environment must also encourage unorthodox thinking.

In this same connection we must consider the supervisor who is afraid of his subordinates. Many supervisors are unwilling to employ a highly competent person out of fear that their positions will become insecure. There is also the overbearing type of superior who tends to crush the initiative and originality of his subordinates. At the other extreme is the submissive type of individual whose direction can be described as laissez faire. All these superiors will effectively discourage the creative abilities of their subordinates and erect a barrier to the communication of good ideas in a vertical direction.

Those who have adolescent children will be keenly aware of the role of the parent in eliciting the maximum rate of intellectual and emotional growth. What is required for effective results in raising a child is the rare ability to maintain a warm, accepting, tolerant, and encouraging attitude, while keeping the reins taut to provide continuing reassurance to the youngster, thereby encouraging him to develop self-confidence. The degree of tension on the reins will vary markedly from individual to individual. In general, it is inversely proportional to the degree of emotional maturity in the adolescent. These principles apply as well to supervision in general and to research administration in particular.

EXPEDITING CREATIVE WORK

Creative thinking gives the impression of being a very wasteful, inefficient, and illogical process. Moreover, the need for a new product is often very urgent. Accordingly, pressure is frequently applied to creative workers. The word produces horror in many creative people, but one cannot help being impressed by the many creative discoveries and developments which occurred under the extreme patriotic urgency developed during World War II. The bridge between these two points of view lies in the realization that creative effort is given spontaneously—it cannot be extracted or taken away from the creative person.

Possibilities for expediting creative work must be looked at from two points of view: the kind of creative work to be pushed and the methods used to achieve the results. My own conviction is that there is an inverse relationship between the scope of a creative work and the extent to which pressure will be effective. In other words, I believe that no amount or kind of outside pressure could have hurried Einstein in developing his insight into the relationship between mass and energy. On the other hand, it is possible to expedite the output of a writer, an artist, or a research scientist. The highly competitive petroleum industry, for example, made considerable progress in conducting crash programs for the purpose of developing new products and processes—for example, an aerosol insecticide dispenser or an improved catalyst for making aromatic hydrocarbons.

A simple analogy may be useful in visualizing these differences. Innumerable impressions are stored away in our unconscious mind. New connections are made by taking what may be called àn imaginative leap. If the leap is a short one—and this is often all that is necessary in new product development—it seems possible to decrease the incubation period by producing in the creative thinker a sense of urgency or a feeling of moderate tension. As a result, the frequency of the imaginative leaps is increased, and the time required for producing a useful association is shortened. The longer the leap that is necessary, however, the less is the probability that a truly creative result will be obtained. Consequently, urgency or tension, while it may increase the frequency of leaps, is likely to produce frustration. This in turn will discourage further effort. If product ideas of broad scope are desired, the manager may have no choice but to wait until the necessary incubation period has elapsed.

THE USE OF GROUPS

The use of groups in creative activities is becoming more frequent in expediting product development and also in stimulating creativity in other phases of business. These groups may be organized in either of two ways. They may consist of representatives of various scientific disciplines for the purpose of obtaining a variety of points of view on a problem area. Again, they may be made up of individuals having demonstrated skill in one or more phases of the creative process. The former approach is clearly the technique used in operations research. Its application presupposes the availability of an abundance of highly creative people with various backgrounds. The latter approach is necessary in smaller organizations less generously blessed with creative talent because it leads to most efficient utilization of available talent.

One value of a group in creative work lies in maintaining a certain degree of tension or pressure. The tension generated intensifies concentration on the problem and increases the frequency of imaginative leaps. In group work it is possible to lower censorship barriers by persuading the members to postpone critical judgment while thinking up and expressing new ideas. Mutual reinforcement by members of the group aids in releasing the brakes on the imaginations of the individuals. The net result is a greater volume of ideas for critical review. These are the more important factors operating in the brainstorming technique.

To be successful in this type of activity, the groups must be made up of participants of approximately the same status in the organization. The presence of a line superior can have a dampening effect. On the other hand, competition or rivalry is always present and, I believe, is responsible for much of the tension which is developed. This rivalry is useful up to a point. It is not uncommon, however, for one or more participants to get an idea and suddenly adopt a defensive attitude. Ideas from other group members become threats against which the first idea must be defended. When ideas are allowed to become weapons in a competitive game or struggle, progress will be slow indeed.

Avoidance of such difficulties calls for considerable skill on the part of the group leader, whose role is most important. He needs not only an understanding of the motivational and environmental forces we have been considering, but also a feeling for human relationships in general.

GUIDELINES TO FOLLOW

1. Creative work is always given spontaneously; it cannot be extracted.
2. The creative worker must be made secure and encouraged to develop self-confidence to the maximum.
3. The creative worker must have an adequate background of factual knowledge in his field of work. He must also be thoroughly familiar with the policy framework within which he can operate.
4. The creative thinker must be free to communicate with those having useful knowledge, points of view, and ideas.
5. Warm encouraging acceptance on the part of the supervisor always stimulates creative output.
6. Some guidance must be supplied in the form of constructive criticism. Many creative people need the reassurance of gentle tension on the reins.
7. A feeling of urgency on the part of the supervisor is perceived by the researcher and will be imitated. Urgency must not be confused with anxiety.
8. Competitive drives can be utilized to create tension or a feeling of urgency. This technique is well adapted to use in group situations. Excessive competition, however, has a negative effect.

We have reviewed a number of impressions of the creative person, some of the factors which motivate him, and environmental and emotional factors which tend to encourage or discourage creative effort. It is clear that we can improve our own creative ability if we wish. It is also generally agreed that solutions to *specific* problems, including many encountered in the development of new products, may be expedited by group creative efforts. There is, however, no substitute for the highly creative individual working in an ideal environment. Certainly, without this combination we cannot have basic or fundamental research. Only the gifted individual can make successful, long-range, imaginative leaps, and only the ideal environment will permit the long incubation necessary for the emergence of great ideas and important new concepts.

SCIENTIFIC MANAGEMENT IN SCIENCE •

BURTON F. BARROWS

THE TERM SCIENTIFIC MANAGEMENT perhaps requires qualification. Inasmuch as it implies that such management embodies scientific principles which can reduce management processes to a quantified methodology, it greatly oversimplifies the total picture. Management, in the final analysis, is an art, and there must be no confusion on this point. But it is an art that, in practice, can and does benefit from application of the basic principles of the scientific method. Management of research and development, unlike industrial management, has failed to realize this, however. Paradoxically, it is the scientist-manager in research and development who is responsible for this failure. He has not understood the very principles that have shaped his life.

The difference between the scientist and the manager must be accepted as fact. The methodology of science is one of exhaustive detail. Decisions are not made by scientists; they are made for them by an accumulation of indisputable facts, arranged so that they leave no element of doubt as to the truth of the hypothesis. This difference is so essential to the true scientist that it shapes all of his thought processes. The manager, on the other hand, is by nature a gambler. In the course of making a decision, he must objectively weigh every fact pertinent to the decision to be made, explore the implications of the decision, and evaluate subjective elements, even if they seem extraneous to the situation. However, in the end, he must recognize the necessity for timing. He must know when to cease relying on fact and fall back upon his own considered judgment.

Another important difference between the scientist and the professional manager concerns their personal objectives. Among outstanding scientists, few have chosen to prepare themselves for management in the academic and postacademic portions of their careers. It is significant that among

---

BURTON F. BARROWS is President and General Manager, SYSTEC, Inc., Walnut Creek, California.

themselves scientists tend to apologize for having taken on management responsibilities, viewing it as a lessening rather than an enhancement of the professional image. On the other hand, all professional managers actively prepare themselves to assume management responsibilities. Few, however, would presume to direct a research project in pattern-recognition logic or in nuclear interactions in thin emulsions, for example.

THE NEGLECT OF THE PROFESSIONAL MANAGER

Nevertheless, top management positions in research and development are filled for the most part by scientists, many of whom not only are incompetent managers but, if they take their management responsibilities seriously, can no longer claim to be capable scientists. The professional manager has virtually no place in top management in this vastly important field, particularly in Government-sponsored projects. An understanding of how scientists have come to assume the function of manager is important as a guide to corrective action.

In its short history, the Manhattan Project initiated and accelerated the emergence of the scientist from the classroom and the laboratory and placed upon his shoulders the collective mantle of industrial leader, states-man, and tactician—a heady mixture for the humble and heretofore largely ignored theoretician or technician. Accustomed to the subsistence-level budgets of prewar research and development, he suddenly found himself empowered to spend millions for which there was little or no accounting. Scientists, as a class, became so endowed with brilliance in the public mind that the word "brilliant" is now almost automatically associated with the term "scientist" as applied to an individual. We can hardly blame the poor scientist for beginning to believe in this description himself and for perpetuating the idea as a tradition.

It is not strange that under such circumstances top management respon-sibility in science was transferred to scientists or that in the discharge of this responsibility scientists should consider as totally unnecessary the advice of nontechnical professional managers. We should not be surprised, therefore, that the incidence of employment of nontechnical, management-oriented personnel is disproportionately low and almost totally confined to the nondecision-making echelons of administrative organization or that the quality of morale and capability among such individuals is inordinately low.

What are the major problems which arise from this predominance of scientist-managers in research and development? In broad terms, some of the logical outgrowths of such a situation are:

1. A failure to define organizational objectives and the confusion of organizational objectives with research objectives.
2. A failure to define management responsibility as distinguished from technical responsibility. This creates a situation in which nontechnical administrators are considered as facilitative in function and technical administrators "manage" in the sense of providing technical leadership. This leaves a vacuum in the area of executive decision making.
3. An almost total breakdown in functional organization planning and, consequently, in internal communications. This results from an inherent stratification of personnel into technical and nontechnical categories, with the nontechnical people relegated to a never-never land generally labeled "support services."
4. The almost universal tendency in research and development to utilize technical people in functions for which they are not trained, ranging from "parts chasing" to top management. This situation alone bleeds off an immeasurable amount of talent so vitally essential.
5. The attitude that justifications, fiscal progress reports, cost accounting procedures, job evaluations, budget reports, and so forth are necessary only to keep the auditors and Government watchdogs at bay but unimportant because they are nontechnical in nature. This viewpoint is costing the Government untold millions of dollars.
6. The tendency on the part of most research and development organizations to meet the frequent problem of overspent (usually spoken of as "underfunded") budgets by cutting back on support personnel while maintaining large numbers of scientists and technicians to preserve a "basic capability for research." This adds to the problem of the nonutilization of technical people.

In order to bring another major problem of management in research and development into focus, we must examine the history of the phenomenal growth in research and development that occurred in the years after World War II, a growth brought about by the exigencies of war and the threat of war. During World War II it was necessary to give our scientists free rein in their monumental efforts to make advances in every area of a generally stagnant technology. One cannot quarrel with the means and certainly not with the end. However, we must remember that large-scale research and development as we know it today, with its multibillion-dollar budgets, developed initially in a free-spending climate engendered by the war. Subsequent development was given impetus by the threat of war and a closely related race in space. While such a climate produces substantial gains in the advancement of science, it is not one conducive to the development of sound fiscal management practices.

SOLUTIONS TO THE PROBLEM

What can be done about these problems? First, and most important, is the re-education of the scientist. He must realize that the professional manager is a valuable man who can not only relieve him of many tedious chores but, more important, significantly increase the purchasing power of available funds. We must assume that the scientist becomes a manager not because he likes to manage but because he honestly feels that he is the only one who can make intelligent decisions with regard to technical work. To gain his confidence, one must learn to talk his language, which in turn implies a basic training in science. In acquiring this basic training, however, there should be no confusion as to objectives. The technical foundation is laid to provide a broader base upon which to build a capability for management. It will require profound dedication to complete a university curriculum in science as well as comprehensive courses in management, but it is essential to do so.

An important obstacle to better management in science is the misconception that *all* Government-sponsored research and development is bound up with the national security. This false idea exists partly because there *is* an element of national security in much of this work, but mainly because there is rarely any one individual or group at any given level of effort having sufficient knowledge of actual security requirements to evaluate program objectives in terms of realistic security criteria and make decisions accordingly.

C. P. Snow has this to say on the subject:

> The euphoria of secrecy goes to the head very much like the euphoria of gadgets. I have known men, prudent in other respects, who became drunk with it. It induces an unbalancing sense of power. It is not of consequence whether one is hugging to oneself a secret about one's own side or about the other. It is not uncommon to run across men, superficially commonplace and unextravagant, who are letting their judgment run wild because they are hoarding a secret about the other side—quite forgetting that someone on the other side, almost indistinguishable from themselves, is hoarding a precisely similar secret about them. It takes a very strong head to keep secrets for years and not go slightly mad. . . . It isn't wise to be advised by any one slightly mad.*

In project organization there is an irresistible tendency toward proliferation. This tendency has a snowball effect as new approaches to a problem

---

* *Science and Government,* Harvard University Press, Cambridge, 1961.

are suggested or as new problems arise. What may start as a small research group can easily grow into an organizational monster, the elements of which so successfully observe the secrecy requirement that they lose communication with or even awareness of each other. If an experiment fails or, as often happens, becomes so hopelessly entangled in effort that it must of necessity fall under its own weight, the remnants can always be swept under the corner of the secrecy carpet. A more serious aspect of secrecy, however, is the increasingly common practice of committing substantial sums of money to projects, justifiably or unjustifiably classified as secret, administered solely by individuals unskilled in fiscal management.

The problem of information management relates to that of secrecy. Senator Hubert Humphrey, who sponsored a Congressional appraisal of information management, has said: "The Federal Government's Model-T methods of managing scientific information contribute to unknowing duplication and tragic and intolerable waste of men, money, and material." Citing the fact that there is no indexed interagency inventory of an estimated 160,000 research projects involving some $8.1 billion, a committee report on Government research projects which were canceled in the past three years states that no serious effort was made to salvage the information developed in completed portions of the canceled projects. Another committee publication on information control in Federally supported electronics research and development projects stated that unknowing duplication in this area alone may cost $200 million a year.

Government-sponsored R&D differs from industrial R&D in three particulars. First, Government projects have a size and complexity impossible in private enterprise. Second, the management of these projects is almost completely in the hands of scientist-managers. Third, many assume therefore that these projects cannot be held accountable for performance and be subject to evaluation in the same way that industrial projects are. However, these problems are not insoluble, and the application of principles proved in industrial management will go far in providing a solution.

If the effectiveness of the billions we are spending on research could be increased only a small percentage, the rewards would be tremendous. It is my conviction that with intelligent planning and effective execution and with the release rather than the capture of the capabilities of science by using proven principles of scientific management and the talents of the professional manager, the purchasing power of our research dollar in Government as well as private industry could be at least doubled.

If we are to fulfill the great promise of today's technologies, we must regain our balance and our perspective. Now, more than ever before, we need to utilize fully all of the skills and knowledge available. The scientist, the engineer, and the businessman must establish an interdisciplinary relationship. Each must understand and reinforce in collective action the drives and objectives of the others in attainment of a common goal. Many responsible scientists recognize this, but the first steps must be taken with conscious effort to utilize fully the methodology of scientific management and the capabilities of professional managers.

CONSERVATION OF SCIENTIFIC MANPOWER •

ESTILL I. GREEN

O N ALL SIDES TODAY WE HEAR about the need to augment our supply of scientists and engineers. Charles F. Kettering once observed: "The reason we have a shortage of scientists and engineers is that today it takes five highly educated persons to do what one low-grade fellow could do 50 years ago." We use our scientific talent with distressing prodigality, and, at best, any substantial improvement in the number of technical personnel available will take time—lots of time. Meanwhile, what—if anything—can be done?

THE USE OF TECHNICAL AIDES

Probably the first and most obvious way to conserve available scientific personnel is to *reduce the diversion of professional talent to nonprofessional activities*. This suggestion means the delegation of subprofessional jobs to subprofessional people, clerical jobs to clerical people, minor administrative jobs to administrative assistants, and so on. A lot of progress in this direction has already been made.

Technical aides range from high school graduates who are given special training to graduates of technical institutes, training courses, and the like, who also get special training as a rule. Women are also an important part of the picture; the only complaint with the women is that they don't stay long enough. The probable stay of a newly hired female technical aide is about two and a half years.

These technical aides are used in many functions: research, exploratory development, development for manufacture, systems engineering, and

ESTILL I. GREEN is an engineering management consultant, Short Hills, New Jersey.

specifications and quality assurance work. Their activities call for a wide range of abilities and skills. For example, technical aides are utilized to:
1. Design, construct, and maintain laboratory test equipment.
2. Evaluate materials, devices, and processes.
3. Design, construct, and evaluate experimental apparatus and development models.
4. Conduct mathematical studies and computations.
5. Make field studies.
6. Analyze field complaints.
7. Prepare specifications and instructions.

Just as it is important to use the professional man to his full ability, so each technical aide should be given work commensurate with his talents; otherwise, there are likely to be frustrations and high turnover.

The real training problem involved in the use of technical aides is to train professional people to *use* the technical aides. It's the kind of training that can't be imparted in classes. It has to be absorbed gradually. What it amounts to is training the professional man to delegate some of his work.

CLERICAL ASSISTANCE

Some progress has been made in relieving professional people of clerical work. One of the difficulties encountered in research and development activity is that a considerable part of the clerical work that might be delegated occurs as a multiplicity of small random parcels emanating from large numbers of people. Moreover, the man who requires the clerical work often needs to follow its execution rather closely. These factors make it hard to organize the clerical help on an efficient basis. What must be done is to assign the clerical assistance to a large enough unit of the organization so that there is a fairly stable workload, but in close enough relation to the individual scientist to permit whatever direction is needed.

How far can we go in the delegation of subprofessional and clerical work? A rough survey suggests that, despite the progress of recent years, somewhere between one-third and one-quarter of our professional personnel's time is spent on work that could be done by technical aides, with a somewhat smaller amount spent on work that could be performed by clerks or secretaries. Of course, we cannot reduce these fractions to zero, but we can come much closer than we have in the past. For example, a saving of just 10 per cent of professional people's time would be equivalent to hiring 300 more scientists.

IMPROVED FACILITIES

Another way of alleviating this shortage is to provide *better physical aids for professional people*. Many new kinds of aids have become available in recent years; for example, computers of different types can relieve scientists of a large part of their less imaginative chores. If design rules can be formulated and built in, computers can perfect engineering designs, check them for accuracy, prepare manufacturing information, direct production, test the finished product, and do a host of other things that now absorb the time of professionally trained people.

BETTER PLANNING OF TECHNICAL EFFORT

Also, we should do everything possible to *eliminate useless and wasteful technical effort*. I don't mean that we should curtail fundamental research because it has no obvious application. Nor would I suggest that we abandon all duplicate approaches to important problems. Competition is often the spur to progress. All I suggest is that, in this period of shortage of technical manpower, we examine areas where extravagant duplications or the vain pursuit of decimal points exist—critically and unflinchingly.

For one thing, we could devote more attention to the planning of research and development programs. Through the years, some companies have found it increasingly essential to maintain a separate organization for studying and planning the new systems which should be developed. This activity is called systems engineering. Because of the increasing complexity of communications and because the worthwhile development opportunities being opened up by expanding art are vastly in excess of available manpower, management is relying more and more heavily on systems engineering studies and recommendations in determining its future program.

FURTHER TRAINING OF OLDER SCIENTISTS

A less tangible but perhaps even more fruitful area is the *provision of up-to-date training for older scientists*. Indeed, it is the efforts of this group as a whole that have been responsible for our scientific progress over the years. But some people grow spontaneously; others need help. There are many who, even though they have contributed in part to the advance, have not kept up with it. In almost any organization, we can find large numbers of technical personnel who would be greatly stimulated

—and their effectiveness greatly multiplied—by training in some aspect of the newer scientific wisdom. It is even possible that we might, over the next few years, accomplish more by providing additional training for people who already have professional degrees than we shall be able to do in augmenting the output of new degrees.

MOTIVATING PROFESSIONAL PERSONNEL

My final suggestion is that we *examine the motivations of our professional people* and look for ways of inspiring them to greater accomplishment. The dominant factors in the scientific accomplishment of an individual are challenge and recognition. Further attention to these factors would, I believe, not only increase scientific accomplishment but add to the sum of human happiness.

OUTSIDE HELP FOR RESEARCH •

I. MILTON LE BARON

O VER THE PAST FEW YEARS, *research in business* and *research as a business* have undergone major changes. These changes are predominantly caused by two factors:

1. The tremendous effect of the huge Governmental expenditures in the area of research. This effect varies much with the particular discipline involved.
2. Without question, the average successful research program takes much longer, is more complex, and costs very much more to bring to a satisfactory financial conclusion.

These changes have led both large and small corporations to seek help outside their own physical research facilities.

Multimillion dollar corporations in the same field have gotten together and either pooled information from their own facilities or have contributed to a mutual fund for research to develop the industry in certain technical areas. In most areas, prime contracting research for the Federal Government, followed by subcontracting to specific capable laboratories those portions in which in-house ability is lacking, is quite commonplace. Research effort is becoming a business of such magnitude and scope that it is more and more difficult to maintain adequate technological competence in all necessary fields. This results in more and more research being carried on outside the physical facilities of a given corporation.

WHY USE OUTSIDE FACILITIES?

The decision to seek outside research assistance in new product development may, of course, be based upon any number of considerations,

I. MILTON LEBARON is Manager, Electro-Optics Department, Texas Instruments Incorporated, Dallas, Texas.

depending upon the specific circumstances of the company and the nature of the research effort required. For the purposes of this discussion, however, we shall consider these motivating reasons as falling into four major categories: financial considerations, technical limitations, expediency, and psychological factors.

Financial considerations. All business is financially motivated, and to this extent financial considerations undoubtedly underlie *any* decision to utilize outside research facilities. More directly, however, there are two common economic reasons for seeking outside research assistance: (1) the amount of research necessary in the company's field of interest may not justify the maintenance of a permanent research facility of the size required; and (2) the company may find that certain aspects of its research activity can be more economically performed by outside agencies specializing in those areas. As management examines the company's overall research budget, it is bound to spot certain project costs that would be high if the company did the work itself. If the company is operating under a fairly strict budget and is trying to make its dollar go as far as possible—and what company today is not?—it would do well to consider the services of an independent research organization in such areas.

Technical limitations. There are few companies whose research facilities are entirely adequate to their needs; no company-operated research organization is big enough to include a specialist in every area of investigation related to the company's activities. A short-term project, for example, is likely to call for specialized personnel who may not be on the payroll; it is not good management practice to hire men for short-term research; so the project is farmed out to an independent organization. The current shortage of capable research people is another important technical limitation. If the company has not been able to hire a man with certain specialized abilities, it may, by patronizing an outside research facility, be able to find a man who has the required qualifications and ultimately hire him. Still another common technical limitation arises when a company develops interest in an area outside its general field. If the company is lucky, its research chief will have sense enough to admit that nobody on the research staff knows anything about the subject, and it will go to somebody outside who does.

A useful management technique employing outside research services is "bilateral continuation." When a company is engaged in an important research project that must be completed within a given time, its management is certain to wonder from day to day whether it is on the right track; indeed, it may even begin to question the competence of its research staff. To dispel such doubts, many companies select an outside research organization and set up such projects bilaterally. This can be an excellent tool for the research director, for it provides him a means of checking on the adequacy of his own staff's effort and assures him that the thinking going into it is not being misdirected, either by himself or by others in the organization. If bilateral continuation is carried on properly, with both research groups kept fully informed of the situation at all times, it is an extremely effective process. But when it develops into *multi*lateral continuation, or when communication barriers are created between the two groups working on the project, the result can usually better be described as "discontinuation"—as, for example, in the guided missile program in the past few years.

Expediency. On some research projects, timing is so important that it outweighs all other considerations. Thus, a research director may be told: "This job has to be finished by such and such date. Money is no object, so long as you get it done on time." The obvious solution, of course, is for the research director to avail himself of the services of a private organization. For a product development project with a tight schedule, or for a crash program, an outside research facility is often the ideal solution. It is not generally desirable to organize the company's research operation on a crash-program basis, for such projects are comparatively rare in industry; and when one does come along, it can usually be handled most effectively by breaking up the total research effort into its various elements and dividing these between the company staff and an outside agency.

Psychological factors. By psychological factors—which is, admittedly, somewhat of a catch-all term—I mean generally those motivating forces that are less concrete than financial considerations, technical limitations, or the like. Take, for example, the use of research findings as a sales incentive. Most companies find it difficult to convince anybody of the adequacy of their own research findings—regardless of how good their research organizations may be. In the tobacco industry, for instance, the consumer apparently accepts the company's claims more readily when they are backed up by the opinion of "independent tobacco buyers." In fact, many organizations first make an investigation of this type on their own; then they go to an outside research laboratory and ask to have their findings corroborated for a fee, so that they can use the laboratory's name in their sales program. Finally, outside facilities in the form of a research consultant may be utilized to sell a new project to an important associate. This is the old story of the prophet without honor in his own country.

A somewhat different approach is the use of an outside research organization to provide an independent appraisal of a company's research findings. It has been my experience that such appraisals are sometimes extremely useful.

WHAT FACILITIES ARE AVAILABLE?

There are almost as many types of outside research facilities as there are types of research, and they do not lend themselves readily to classification. It is possible, however, to identify a few of the most commonly used agencies.

Universities. Many of the larger, more progressive universities in the United States have research institutes. These are all independent, nonprofit research organizations, endowed either by private interests or by the Government. The university's faculty represents another important source of outside research assistance. Thus, the company might retain a professor who has specialized in some particular field in which it is interested—organic research, for example—to keep it up to date on new basic research developments. This is one of the least expensive methods of supplementing a company's own research efforts, and I recommend it highly. Professors today are still grossly underpaid, and any additional income the company can provide them will be repaid many times over in the information they gather. Another important benefit of this practice is the encouragement it can provide to those scientists whose primary interest is in the field of basic research.

Nonprofit research institutes. There are a number of large nonprofit research organizations (such as Battelle or Stanford Research Institute) whose staffs include people who are highly competent in a variety of fields. It is very commonly—and erroneously—assumed, however, that because a research institute is competent in one field, it is so in every field. All of these institutes today are trying to improve their facilities. Sometimes, unfortunately, the improvement campaign takes the form of pressure of one sort or another applied on a company's research director to assign a problem to an organization that is not the best qualified to handle it. It pays, therefore, to study the entire situation carefully before coming to a decision, so as to be completely familiar with what the other research institutes can do, what their staffs are like, and how they rate with other companies that have used them.

Profit-making research organizations. Private, profit-making research enterprises are quite similar in concept and operation to the nonprofit organizations. There is little difference between the two types of facilities in the capability of their staffs, the energy of their efforts, or the size of their fees. Generally speaking, the profit-making research organizations are entirely adequate. In most cases, if they feel they are not capable of handling a given project satisfactorily, they will turn it down.

Trade association laboratories. Many industry trade associations maintain laboratories, and some of these will even do research projects for companies outside the particular industry serviced. The names of these laboratories can be obtained from the United States Chamber of Commerce.

Miscellaneous organizations. In this category I would include the vast number of large general consulting organizations that are developing special research services, as well as the many sizable research agencies that have developed from what were originally small consulting services. A careful, thorough study of their facilities and past activities is recommended before using their services.

Government agencies. Although in the past the United States Government has supported some very adequate sources of research assistance (most notably, perhaps, in the TVA program), a number of factors are responsible for a somewhat different situation today: (1) the need for strict security in the vast amount of Government-sponsored research connected with the defense program; (2) the prevailing political climate, which seems to favor a minimum of Government participation in the affairs of private industry; (3) the general distrust of "bureaucratic" Government agencies; and (4) the need to keep the country's research facilities and know-how dispersed in case of enemy attack. In short, the Government simply does not have the kind of research facilities that industry needs. One of the major factors today in the use of Government funds for research and development is the question of patent rights. The attitude of NASA is to be greatly deplored. Government control of research and development is the inevitable result if all developments made on Government funds belong to the Government. Individual incentive will certainly decrease under these controls.

DEALING WITH THE OUTSIDE AGENCY

When the decision has been made to utilize a specific outside facility for research, policy must be translated into action. The first important step is to formulate the problem to be solved. If the project requires basic research only, a fairly general statement of purpose will suffice; if the problem is specific, however, a detailed analysis will be necessary.

The next step is the drawing up of a contract. To avoid later disputes, it is essential that the terms of the contract be clear. This is the responsibility of the company—not of the outside agency. The contract should cover these points:

1. Nature of the research problem.
2. Exact timing of the project.
3. Amount of fee and manner of payment.
4. Responsibility for operating costs (telephone calls, overhead, and the like).

5. Extent of the outside agency's liability in the event that confidential information should be leaked or stolen.
6. Patent structure. (The research agency may prefer to file the patent in its own name first, so that it can point with pride to its accomplishments; it then assigns the patent without fee to the client organization. It is important that any such procedure be covered in detail in the contract.)
7. Applicability of research findings. (The precise extent to which the results of the agency's research efforts are the company's property must be defined in order to prevent the development of future problems in the event that these findings should be applicable to other fields.)
8. Termination procedure.
9. Security precautions.
10. Procedure for reporting to the client.

After the contract has been drawn up and signed, the next step is the selection of the company's liaison man—the most important single factor in the success or failure of a research project involving an outside organization. It is obviously wise to choose somebody for this task who has been with the company for a considerable period. You cannot simply hire a liaison agent from the outside—somebody, let us say, with a great deal of experience in the research area but no familiarity with the company's specific problems. In addition to a thorough understanding of the company's objectives, organization, and operations, the liaison man should also possess an instinctive "feel" for the political aspects of the situation.

When the project is at last actually under way, it is important to leave the agency's contracting researchers alone for a while; they won't have anything to tell you for some time, and they will quite naturally resent your early snooping. Three months is about the right interval between checks on the agency's progress, regardless of how long the project continues. At least once a year the company's top management should get together with the top people of the research agency to get a definite understanding of how the project is going and to decide what directions it should take in the future. Management should be especially careful to avoid needling the agency unnecessarily to get the project done in short order. It must be as fair in its consideration of outside work as it would be of effort within the company.

The big problem confronting a company which is interested in utilizing outside research facilities is not in finding a suitable agency but in choosing the *most suitable* one from among the many possibilities. There is no difficulty in obtaining information about the various facilities available;

all you have to do is let it get out that you're interested, and you'll be flooded with information. With the wide range of outside research facilities available today, there is no need to come to a decision after one meeting with one individual. You can afford to shop around—the price won't change while you do. The important thing is to see that your project is adequately handled.

PROFESSIONAL DEVELOPMENT NEEDS OF THE RESEARCHER •

SIDNEY L. JONES

RESEARCH AND DEVELOPMENT activities have become the key factor in the economic success of many companies. Any evaluation of the corporate research function emphasizes the dependence on quality in the technical staff. As a result of the importance of the individual researcher, personnel directors have a vital interest in the continuous professional development of technical employees. Unfortunately, the managerial controls applied to R&D activities have often been ineffective. Part of the problem arises from the lack of familiarity of most industrial managers with the problems and personnel involved. The fact that most senior executives are trained in the nontechnical phases of the business accentuates the problems of understanding and communication. These uncertainties have often resulted in friction within the laboratories and a failure to develop the R&D capabilities of the staff to their full potential.

A study conducted by the National Society of Professional Engineers found that 56 per cent of the firms surveyed had no training program for newly hired technical graduates, and 66 per cent had no program for experienced men. These percentages have undoubtedly been improved in recent years; nevertheless, the lack of interest is surprising in view of the great emphasis upon the training of industrial employees in other functions. Resignations and requests for transfers by younger staff members are the most obvious and immediate results of a poor program for staff development. Eventual stagnation of the staff and a failure to develop creative research and development results are even more serious consequences. This attitude may be partly attributed to the general belief that scientists and engineers are already highly trained by their formal schooling and that industrial training is unnecessary for professional employees—or even

SIDNEY L. JONES is Assistant Professor of Finance, School of Business, Northwestern University, Evanston, Illinois.

beneath their dignity. This viewpoint fails to consider the rapid pace of developments in technical fields and the individual researcher's interest in continued training. It also ignores the vast amount of experience accumulated within industry and the advantages of training through practical application of knowledge.

In an attempt to provide management with information which can be used in deciding what types of controls to establish in the R&D area, a further study of the reactions of an elite group of technical research employees to various management controls was conducted among 193 leading scientists and engineers from 25 outstanding organizations. Each company was asked to select approximately ten men on the basis of their demonstrated creativity and productivity.

A majority of the research workers interviewed agreed that there is a definite need for additional formal training while they are working in industry. Only a few felt that a program of self-study is adequate to keep pace with the expansion of knowledge. A similar project revealed that a large number were continuing to study in their major field through some formal program, and another large group were formally studying in interest areas outside their specialties.

We all know that a company can assist the individual by offering formal courses and informal on-the-job training within the company; by supporting participation in professional societies; and by stimulating interest in formal academc work outside of the company by granting financial aid and free time for attendance. A majority of the group felt that the company should adopt an *official policy* of providing these opportunities and offer specific encouragement to participate. The minority did not disagree with the goals of the programs, but they argued that the company should adopt a passive attitude and allow the individual to decide what interests to follow. Both groups were emphatic concerning the undesirability of there being any management coercion to join in programs. This is because professional employees normally respond very negatively toward such overt pressure. The comment of one of the interviewees is representative:

> I don't believe that managers can successfully "force-feed" a formal training course to a professional employee, and any such training must be on a voluntary basis. If the program is of a high quality, those who do not participate are voluntarily losing the benefits, and those who receive the training will progress further in their careers.

Members of the sample group did recognize the possibility of indirect pressures being applied in the form of promotion policies, salary adjustments, and merit ratings. Although these indirect forces often achieve the same results as rigid management regulations, threats cannot be substituted for personal motivation, and the effectiveness of any development program will depend upon the individual researcher's attitude. The response of this outstanding group indicated that this personal motivation is present and that they are interested in having management support formal training efforts if coercion is avoided. Table 1 reveals the response to company-sponsored programs.

INTEREST IN TRAINING IN MANAGEMENT SKILLS

Although most types of training should be directed at increasing the professional competence of the staff, there was substantial interest among the members of the sample group in receiving more training in management skills (71 per cent indicated the company should provide more training in this area). However, only 55 per cent answered that this type of training is now provided for R&D employees. Such training for development of interest and competence in handling managerial responsibilities was considered to be particularly important for the younger members of the technical staff who have the desire and aptitude to move into technical administrative positions. A formal training program also allows for promotion from within the R&D group to avoid the damage done to morale and employee loyalty by importing managers from outside sources. Several members of the group made the interesting suggestion that administrative personnel receive some training in research methods to increase their skills and to make them more aware of the problems and opportunities in the R&D field.

The major emphasis is still on continued development in technical fields, with the major areas of suggested improvement to be as follows (ranked in descending order of importance): (1) mathematics, (2) liberal arts and humanities, (3) "subject" courses rather than "theory" courses, (4) theoretical physics, (5) philosophy, (6) study for advanced degree, (7) training in administration and psychology, (8) English and communications, (9) work in fundamental science and engineering, and (10) work in a technical specialty.

Activity	Yes	No	No Response
		(in percentages)	
Technical seminars	79	13	8
Technical conferences	78	19	3
Technical lectures	76	15	9
Technical "short training courses"	54	35	11
Visits to other companies	80	13	7

TABLE 1

INFORMAL ON-THE-JOB TRAINING

Despite the increasing role of formal programs, most training still consists of informal on-the-job orientation. The highly individualized nature of research work requires a high degree of personal freedom. The most common approach is to merely assign junior members of the staff to senior colleagues for their training on the basis of a master-apprentice relationship. This informal arrangement was endorsed in the study as the most meaningful method of training young researchers, especially if the assignments are varied through some system of rotation. A formal sequence of assignments to a variety of problems is one technique for developing a breadth of competence in younger staff members. The problem is to develop both breadth and depth of training in technical fields along with some managerial competence in meeting supervisory and economic problems. An informal working relationship allows the junior man to learn specific details which formal training cannot provide because of its more general content. Apprenticeship training also eliminates much of the regimentation of formal programs. However, this approach should not preclude the use of formal training where the need is apparent. The specific balance varies according to the size of the organization, the type of research performed, and the training objectives.

The reliance upon informal training techniques places a larger burden upon supervisors in assuring that each individual receives the direction and opportunities he needs. Because the approach is informal, there is a danger that the employee's training may be unplanned, superficial, erratic, or outdated unless supervisors constantly analyze the progress of each individual. This problem emphasizes the increased demand for superior management when informal controls are used. It may also be difficult to find enough senior men who have the time and are capable of training junior men.

Where the apprenticeship system is used, it must be carefully controlled to prevent the inbreeding of ideas. Many managements have attempted to avoid this danger by increasing the exchange of information within the organization. The reaction of the sample group in evaluating the worth of these activities was mixed, as is shown by Table 2.

PERSONAL TIME FOR PRELIMINARY INVESTIGATIONS

One form of on-the-job training which received a very favorable reaction was the suggestion that R&D employees be encouraged to investigate their own ideas as differentiated from official company projects. This usually consists of allocating some share of the researcher's time for preliminary investigations of personal interest before formal projects are established.

Activity	Yes	No	No Response
		(in percentages)	
Dinner meetings of the technical staff	52	38	10
Informal luncheons	56	33	11
Staff "gripe sessions"	53	35	12
Wide circulation of the minutes of committee meetings	39	49	12
Wide circulation of technical reports	81	11	8

TABLE 2

This time should be accumulated until a sustained effort can be devoted to avoid confusion among various projects. Approximately three-fourths of the group expressed enthusiastic support of this practice as an effective means of stimulating original thinking. Several others would also favor the policy if the privilege is restricted to senior staff members with proven ability. The alternative of allowing this type of freedom on an informal basis without any official company policy also received some support.

This approach provides for the exploration of interesting problems not covered by official projects and would help reduce the unplanned, bootleg research now conducted informally in many laboratories. Such research can be desirable because it is the result of intense personal motivation. The danger in this is that it may detract from broader laboratory goals which the individual may not recognize. There is also the problem of usurping physical facilities and equipment needed for other projects.

The advantage of granting personal time on an official basis is that the personal motivation is retained and research is brought out into the open where other staff members and management can follow the activity. The increased freedom would add to the professional stature of the R&D staff and would help attract other capable men. It would also be an effective method of stimulating the personal development of individual researchers, particularly junior staff members. This plan provides strong incentives if pressure on individuals is avoided and the specific details are varied according to the maturity and abilities of the employees and the type of research performed. Those already participating in such a plan stressed the benefits to the company and the R&D group. However, managers should avoid applying any broad policy to the entire department without analyzing the individual characteristics of the staff.

The most serious reservation concerned the expense of such a plan if the quality of the staff did not warrant the privilege. Others were dubious that management would be able to define a procedure which would provide the freedom desired and also prevent the possible abuses and excessive costs. Critics also pointed to the failure of most attempts to install this incentive plan because of the lack of interest shown by most R&D workers. Nevertheless, the overwhelming majority felt that providing the opportunity would be very beneficial even though only a few outstanding employees might have the ability and interest to use the privilege. It would also be a general stimulus to the average worker merely to know that the opportunity was available.

PARTICIPATION IN PROFESSIONAL SOCIETIES

Management can also stimulate the continued growth of its R&D staff members by supporting their participation in professional societies. A majority (83 per cent) stressed the value of such participation as a source of personal development and as a means of increasing the professional status and recognition of research employees. Specific benefits referred to are (ranked in descending order of importance):

1. Increases the technical knowledge of the participants.
2. Broadens the background and viewpoint of the R&D staff.
3. Provides an excellent source of new ideas through a stimulating association with colleagues.
4. Increases the motivation of the R&D staff and provides a source of personal satisfaction.
5. Provides an opportunity to stay abreast of new developments in the field prior to official publication.
6. Increases the reputation of the company.
7. Provides for an exchange of knowledge and ideas, which prevents inbreeding.
8. Promotes more professional working attitudes among the R&D staff.
9. Provides a source of valuable contacts for the individual employees.
10. Enables the R&D employees to meet the leaders in their technical fields and receive inspiration from them.

These benefits make it worthwhile for companies to encourage their scientists and engineers to be active, and the majority of the group (73 per cent) agreed that management should actively do this as long as direct coercion is not used (a minority felt that it is unnecessary for the company to officially stimulate activity). Specific support is given by management according to 67 per cent of the sample group.

The only restriction on these outside contacts suggested by the sample group involves the protection of confidential company information dealing with proprietary products. It was generally agreed that management is justified in requesting research employees to limit their discussion of company R&D activities outside of the company. The consensus opinion (88 per cent) was that the company should have some control over the publishing activities of its staff members to prevent the unauthorized disclosure of confidential information. The minority group in both cases felt that the researcher does this automatically without any restrictions so that official policies are unnecessary. There was universal agreement that the company must protect its large financial interest in R&D results for competitive reasons. R&D work requires heavy investments of company resources, and the sample group stressed that companies who support these activities have the right to exploit the results. Therefore, premature publication which reduces the economic advantages should be prevented, especially where patent rights are not clear.

Despite the importance of protecting the company's preferred position, managers should attempt to grant freedom to its staff in its outside activities, and the discretion of the research worker is usually adequate protection. Many commented that companies often make these restrictions unnecessarily tight or keep them in force beyond a reasonable period. It is also important to consider the beneficial effects of exchanging ideas with other organizations. The net benefits of keeping R&D results confidential must be compared with the loss of outside contacts when the exchange of information is eliminated. Consideration should also be given to exchanging information in fundamental research areas.

RECOGNITION OF PROFESSIONAL CONTRIBUTIONS

Along with the personal satisfaction of achieving individual improvement, research employees need to know how their work affects the organization and how well they are performing their functions. The assumption that scientists and engineers derive all of their job satisfactions out of personal evaluations of their own professional achievements is incorrect. To create an emotional commitment to the goals of the laboratory, the staff needs the security and guidance of external evaluation. Without an emotional attachment, each assignment becomes a "job" with a financial reward. The creative person also wants the intangible rewards of knowing his work is important, that he is contributing to goals which are broader than self-gratification, and that his peers recognize and admire his efforts. In the institutionalized laboratories of modern industry, the "peer group" extends beyond the R&D staff into other departments and includes the top administrative leaders of the company. Managers who ignore the communication of this knowledge to their professional staff destroy one of the most stimulating motivations available to leaders—the warm reaction of an employee to an external expression of human interest and recognition of his individual worth.

The different professional goals and working techniques of researchers combined with the intangible nature of the bulk of research findings make the traditional forms of job evaluation very difficult; but the nature of research emphasizes the importance of such efforts because of the high value of the professional staff. It was discouraging to find that only 60 per cent of the sample group felt that they do understand how their work relates to company goals, and only 67 per cent were satisfied with the efforts of supervisors to appraise their performance. Less than half of the group felt that top management was aware of their contributions despite their selection to participate in this study. These responses clearly indicate the need for improved communication.

The use of performance rating techniques to compare individuals against the absolute standards of the job and against other employees on a relative basis is one way of communicating. Merit ratings often develop norms of average behavior and screen out misfits by assigning quantitative values to characteristics even though the evaluations are largely subjective. The twin dangers in attempting to apply merit rating techniques in the laboratory are the tendency toward excessive formality in striving to establish averages and the difficulty in recognizing the unique contributions of the creative worker. A little over half agreed that a formal system of merit rating may be useful in identifying personal goals and deficiencies; nevertheless, there was little faith that such techniques would be able to recognize outstanding research accomplishments. There was a definite agreement that the merit rating procedures used in other parts of the company would not cover the job requirements of the research facility and would include many irrelevant factors.

Attempts to quantify the contributions of researchers in terms of number of problems solved, savings or sales resulting from projects, number of patents, and number of publications were particularly criticized. A simple numerical total of such activities is not a valid measure because of the team nature of modern research, the long time periods required for research, and the wide dispersion of quality. The practice of churning out meaningless articles and patents is as prevalent in industry as it is in the universities. Attempts to rank the quality of these contributions reintroduces the subjective element. Qualitative measures of knowledge, years of schooling, loyalty, and conformity are equally poor measures for determining the contribution of the individual to the group.

It appears that job evaluations will have to continue to be based on the traditional subjective measures now in use. No extensive use of checklists based on average levels of performance was found in the laboratories. It is clear that definite improvements in communication are needed and that more emphasis should be placed on the unique capabilities required of a research worker as measured by the scope and depth of his knowledge and

Characteristic	Times Mentioned
1. Productivity and performance	34
2. Creativity, imagination, originality, insight	27
3. Research competence; analytical and logical knowledge of technical field	22
4. Cooperation, attitude, enthusiasm, sincerity	21
5. Perseverance, attainment of goals, reliability, self-discipline, thoroughness	19
6. Suggestions to management leading to new products	19
7. Initiative, responsibility, curiosity	8
8. Leadership characteristics, maturity, judgment	7
9. Ability to communicate ideas	6
10. Publications and patents (combined)	5
11. Personality factors	4
12. Professional integrity	3
13. Education and experience (combined)	2
14. Miscellaneous group	13
Total	190

TABLE 3

his current output in terms of quality and quantity. Table 3 is an attempt at compiling a list of characteristics for merit rating in R&D facilities. Despite the wide range of qualities suggested, the results are significant in emphasizing the intangible aspects of research.

* * *

The responses of this outstanding group indicate that it is possible for the company to contribute to the development of the professional employee in industry. There is a definite need for continuous formal training, and a variety of different techniques are available for achieving this goal. Research workers require the excitement of a challenge to provide an emotional attachment to their duties. Part of the challenge involves keeping abreast of the state of the art in the technical fields. Industrial managers have the responsibility of sponsoring some of these training activities and of encouraging the members of the technical staff to participate. At the same time, managers must avoid direct and indirect coercion which infringes on the professional status of the research worker. The proper degree of encouragement is difficult to determine because of the possible dangers of employee resentment. Nevertheless, the benefits of having the technical staff participate in formal training programs on a continuous basis are worth the efforts of management in terms of improved research creativity and productivity

THE EVALUATION OF RESEARCH •

W. D. SEYFRIED

R ESEARCH IS NOW AN IMPORTANT function in most businesses and is actually becoming a big business itself. Over the past 20 years, expenditures in the United States for research and development have increased so much that if the present trend continues, spending over the next five-year period could be in excess of $100 billion. Obviously, expenditures of this magnitude must be subject to some sort of evaluation; we cannot accept them on faith. This applies to Government-sponsored as well as business-supported research.

The management of a company supporting a research effort is certainly entitled to know, and *should* know, whether it is getting its money's worth from research and development. It must know how effective its research is and must have some means of comparing research expenditures with other investment opportunities, including the alternative of buying the results of research conducted by others. One of the striking features about the literature on the subject is the practically unanimous agreement on one point—that there is no universally applicable method of appraising research. In spite of this, however, nearly everyone agrees that it is essential to make an attempt at evaluation.

It is impossible to discuss research evaluation intelligently without also discussing research (and business) planning and organization, since all these subjects are closely interrelated. The best definition of research evaluation that I have found describes it as "the process of judging past perform-ance for the purpose of guiding future action." If we accept this definition,

W. D. SEYFRIED is Manager of Research, Humble Oil & Refining Company, Houston, Texas.

we can see why it is impossible to separate evaluation from planning and organization in an attempt to evaluate research.

THE PURPOSE OF RESEARCH EVALUATION

The purpose of research evaluation is to guide future actions involving both business and research decisions. These decisons include such things as how much should be spent on research, how the research money should be allocated, what the priorities should be, how research results should be exploited, and how business and research objectives should be integrated. It has been my company's experience that proper evaluation of research is essential to research planning. Furthermore, proper evaluation helps avoid or reduce wasted effort and leads to the establishment of guidelines for measuring effectiveness and efficiency.

Objective appraisal often points the way to more effective cooperation between research and other functions of the company. Since failure to commercialize a product or process or to utilize research in other ways is not always the fault of the research organization, evaluation sometimes produces unexpected dividends in other phases of company operations. For example, a study of some of our research projects led to the conclusion that a great deal of time and money was being wasted in the translation of research results into commercial projects. An analysis of the reasons for this led to the establishment of a "project manager" system which involved the appointment of a manager to handle all phases of promising research projects from research and development through engineering and construction to actual operations. This manager has complete responsibility for the project and can draw freely upon all parts of the organization for help. The adoption of this system has not only shortened the time needed to complete projects but has also produced significant economies in manpower and capital investment.

When properly conducted, research evaluation helps keep research people on their toes and assures them of management's interest in their activities. If not properly conducted, however, it can be self-defeating. There have been cases when research evaluation has been accomplished in such a manner that the research people regarded it as more of a witch hunt than as an objective appraisal. They reacted in a defensive manner and wasted much effort proving the validity of their positions. On other occasions, attempts at evaluation have resulted in wasteful and damaging arguments about who should really get the credit for a particular project. Obviously, if we give all the credit to research without recognizing the essential contributions from other departments of the company, cooperation can be very difficult to achieve.

THE RESPONSIBILITY FOR EVALUATION

There is much difference of opinion on the question of who should evaluate research, and actual practice varies considerably for different organizations. One of the fundamental problems seems to be whether research should be evaluated internally, by the research people themselves, or externally, by members of management, who are essentially the customers for research results. Research management is certainly in the best position to assess research from a technical standpoint, while business management is in a better position to appraise it from a monetary point of view. It has been the general experience of my company that research should be evaluated by both working together. This also applies to research planning.

It is often said that a primary responsibility of business management is to provide information on business trends, production and financial forecasts, and the like to help guide research into areas where technology is needed. The major responsibility of research people, then, is to supply the needed technology. All of this is quite true, but it does not go far enough. A major weakness in this type of approach is the fact that technology often drastically affects business trends and forecasts so that there is a great deal of interplay. Only by developing the proper interrelationships can the best results be obtained both for research and for the company as a whole.

We feel strongly that research is an essential and powerful tool for achieving the company's short- and long-term objectives and that every effort should be made to use it effectively in our operations. In order to achieve maximum effectiveness, we feel it essential to create the proper atmosphere to assure cooperation between the business and research elements of the company. To accomplish this, we must establish well-defined responsibilities and objectives. My company is large and complex, and research is conducted in connection with many operations: exploration, oil production, manufacturing, marketing, and petrochemicals. Most of these areas encompass the entire spectrum of research from long-range, fundamental, and exploratory studies to development, engineering, and technical service. We conduct our own research and also contract for it with affiliated and outside organizations.

In such a situation research responsibilities must be defined just as carefully as other business responsibilities. The highest executive in each major function of our business is held responsible for research as it affects his operations just as he is held responsible for other aspects of the business. The corporate manager of research has the responsibility for the overall balance of the research program and for all aspects of research that are supported on a corporate rather than a departmental basis. The job of the departmental executives is to define the needs and opportunities in their areas, to communicate them to the research people, to negotiate a research program and budget, and to evaluate and apply the results. Appropriate research people develop the program and budget, taking into account the needs and opportunities of the business departments, and carry out the program as agreed upon. The research people are also responsible for evaluating the effectiveness of the business departments in applying research results. Suitable checks and balances are incorporated to resolve disputes, should they occur, and to prevent the research program from becoming either a mere technical service or an area too isolated from business operations.

Obviously, the establishment of such responsibilities, while essential, is not enough—particularly when one believes as we do that the individual researchers must make the primary contributions to the program. For this reason, each of the various functions has research advisers to assure communications at all levels and to encourage the growth of the program from its initiation to its conclusion.

THE TIME TO EVALUATE

The evaluation may concern work already completed or work yet to be started. Actually, of course, the two are closely related, because a major purpose of postevaluation is to provide a reasonable guide for the planning of future programs. As far as we are concerned, then, both evaluation and planning should be done concurrently.

Even if we accept this concept, it is not easy to answer the question of when to evaluate, because the answer also varies with what is being evaluated. In our company we evaluate the overall program once a year and certain major projects almost continuously. The annual review of the overall program sets targets and budget objectives for the coming year. It is supplemented throughout the year by more detailed reviews of individual areas. In certain cases involving quality problems and the introduction of new products, where technology is often needed in a hurry, priority decisions have to be made on almost a day-to-day basis. On major development projects where a number of functions are involved, we have to reappraise the project frequently as new data come in and new problems arise. We believe that the feedback principle should be used to its fullest extent in research work and that it is a great mistake to adhere too rigidly to a given program if the development of new technology or circumstances dictate a change. For some types of investigation, however, such as long-range and exploratory research, we feel that the program should not be changed too rapidly, once objectives have been defined and the program agreed upon, because in our experience the off-again, on-again approach is often self-defeating in the development of long-range technology.

THE METHOD OF EVALUATING

An old dilemma exists in choosing a method of appraisal: management is concerned with evaluating research in terms of dollars, while research is concerned with the development of technology which must be translated into dollars. How, for instance, do we evaluate some new product or process that has been developed with the full concurrence of management but which for some reason remains unused?

There are a number of techniques available. Admittedly, many of them are inadequate, and some areas of research defy any type of quantitative evaluation, but we must remember that this problem is not restricted to research activities.

Techniques for research evaluation can be divided into three categories: quantitative, qualitative, and integrated. The first two are self-explanatory, but the third may require some definition. The term "integrated" implies that research is best appraised by how well the research program is integrated into the overall company structure and objectives. In other words, research is simply an integral part of the company's organization, and it is best appraised by how well it helps the company achieve its objectives through the development and application of technology related to those objectives. It is apparent, then, that integration is really dependent upon acceptance of research by the company. This acceptance is in turn based on some form of quantitative or qualitative evaluation, whether performed consciously or unconsciously.

Quantitative evaluation. Most industrial research is susceptible to some form of quantitative analysis. There are many techniques for this kind of evaluation; they range all the way from simple formulas—which use company profits for a given period of time as the numerator and research costs as the denominator—to more sophisticated approaches involving present worth and discounted cash flow. These techniques can be used for the appraisal of either past or future projects. Their usefulness depends upon the accuracy of the data or the assumptions used in the formula. Fairly accurate data are usually available, but in *preappraisal* such techniques must be used with a great deal of caution because of the many imponderables that must go into the formula: probability of technical and marketing success for products and so forth. Quantitative techniques are useful to varying degrees when evaluating new products and processes, new uses for old products, process improvements, royalty income gained or saved as the result of patents, and capital-investment savings.

In applying quantitative techniques, however, there are certain pitfalls to be avoided. One of these is that quantitative predictions of profits from certain research projects which seem to be based on valid assumptions sometimes fail to materialize to the degree anticipated (often because the expected earnings are passed on to the customer), with the result that management may lose confidence in such forecasts. We are frequently tempted to concentrate research in areas where the risk is low and some profit is almost assured. This means that other projects having a higher risk but a much larger potential for the company are de-emphasized. It is certainly one of management's primary responsibilities to see to it that long-term opportunities are not sacrificed unduly for short-term advantages.

Some of the more sophisticated techniques are frequently more time consuming than is justified by the data, and they can give misleading results. For instance, rigid application of the concept of discounted cash flow can sometimes result in the conclusion that a particular area of exploratory research should be discontinued because the immediate value to the company is quite low, whereas further examination would reveal that the situation would be reversed in five to ten years. Nevertheless, this particular technique has been quite useful to us in reaching priority decisions, particularly on major development projects. However, it must be borne in mind that such techniques are only tools and must be combined with judgment.

Qualitative evaluation. This kind of analysis could also be called subjective evaluation. It is usually based on the considered judgment of a group of qualified and responsible management people. There are certain types of research where this is really the only technique that can be usefully applied. These include long-range or fundamental research; certain aspects of quality research; research efficiency; and the intangible products of research such as publications, public relations, and the like. Even here, however, it is frequently possible to set up certain yardsticks which can be used (at least for semiquantitative evaluation): comparisons with the results obtained by competitors or by others within the company, the relationship of achievements to stated objectives, and others.

In the long run, of course, it should be possible to arrive at a quantitative evaluation of the total research effort, including the intangibles, if we take the viewpoint that all phases of research contribute eventually to the ultimate product of research—technology that can be translated to and measured in terms of dollars. The real problem then becomes one of balance between the various major categories of research. Over a sufficient period of time, even the fundamental and exploratory aspects of research can be judged as to whether they have provided sufficient new technology and ideas to yield useful projects for development and application.

*   *   *

We attempt to use a combination of all available techniques, from fairly detailed quantitative evaluation in the case of major development projects to qualitative or semiquantitative judgments in the case of long-range projects. In the final analysis, we have found that there is no substitute for judgment exercised by qualified, responsible people. The total research program is composed of a large number of parts, all of which are subject to some degree of evaluation. The best way to assure that the overall program is sound is to exercise the best possible judgment on each part. In short, the evaluation of the research effort will depend upon how well it provides, at minimum cost, the technology, processes, and products needed to help define and achieve the company's functional and corporate objectives and on how well it provides opportunities for growth and profit through the development of new technology.

CRITERIA FOR THE EVALUATION OF INDUSTRIAL SCIENTIFIC RESEARCH •

RALPH E. BURGESS

INDUSTRIAL SCIENTIFIC RESEARCH may be defined as *an organized effort on the part of a company to provide itself with the technology it needs for its present and future growth.* I prefer this definition primarily because it ties research to certain broad—but definite—objectives. Stated in more general terms, the objectives of industrial scientific research are to add to the world's basic knowledge and to improve the living standard of the general public and of the firm's employees and owners. A more narrow objective, which in my opinion does not go far enough toward accepting public responsibility, is to improve the firm's return to its stockholders by way of dividends, capital gains, and stability of earnings.

IMPORTANCE OF INDUSTRIAL RESEARCH

Regardless of how it is measured, the industrial research effort in the United States is impressive. Our total annual expenditure increased from a mere $300 million immediately prior to World War II to nearly $11 billion by 1961. Nearly half of this research was supported by funds from industry.

As is well known, much of the research work financed by the Federal Government is actually performed by private industry or by universities, while some of that supported by industry is farmed out to universities and other nonprofit research institutions. The net effect of such transfers of funds is a rise of nearly 75 per cent in the proportion of research work actually performed by industry.

The nation's total research bill now runs close to $12 billion a year, a sum which is equal to more than 2 per cent of the total value of all goods and services produced (GNP). Students of this subject will be aided in the

---

RALPH E. BURGESS is President, Ralph E. Burgess & Associates, Wilton, Connecticut.

future by more complete and more frequently published statistical reports planned by the Bureau of the Census and other Government agencies.

It is obvious that a rapidly growing activity of this magnitude is bound to exert an important influence on our national economy. In addition, research expenditures affect the growth of entire industries, as well as of individual companies. Let us examine each of these briefly.

IMPORTANCE TO THE NATION

Research is of importance to the nation primarily because it promotes economic growth. It has been estimated that more than one-third of the improvement in the standard of living in this country since 1929 may be attributed in part to successful technological innovations. However, it would not do for those engaged in research to claim all the credit for the development of new products and processes. The results of research must be exploited, and new products must be brought from the laboratory to the home of the average consumer—for which tasks substantial amounts of labor, capital, and managerial talent are essential. The contribution to progress made by each of these additional ingredients is, of course, a major one. Nevertheless, the laboratory result is the initiating factor— the catalyst—for all that follows.

Technological discoveries also disclose profitable new areas for investment, which can serve as outlets for savings. Well-managed business firms —and families—plan on spending less than their total incomes and investing the remainder. Unless such savings do find outlets, either directly or through the channel of financial institutions, the funds remain idle and constitute a drag on the economy.

Research activity on the current scale serves as an important stabilizing force in the economy, not only through the indirect effects noted above, but also in a more direct manner. The results of research bring on (or, at least, hasten) the obsolescence of products, processes, and whole industries; at the same time, they provide replacement for those elements that are so displaced. Moreover, the level of total research expenditures is not directly affected by business fluctuations, and it remains fairly stable from year to year. Businessmen recognize the need for continuing research activities on the customary scale—even during a business recession— so that they will be able to compete when industrial activity turns up again. In promoting diversification of products and interests, research further stabilizes the economy, for a firm is thus enabled to avoid putting all its eggs in one basket.

Another important general benefit derived from research is the assistance it provides in developing a more efficient use of our limited natural resources. And when international tension is high, as at present, research constitutes a vital asset in the competitive battle for national security. Thus, by all the available criteria for judging the importance of an activity to the nation, research receives a high rating.

IMPORTANCE TO INDUSTRY

In considering the contribution made by research to the welfare of an industry, it is important to note that there exists a clear link between industrial growth and research. While the latter is not the sole determinant of the former, it is an essential element. In various industries, there is a rather close relationship between the rate of growth in output and the ratio of research expenditures to sales. The fast-growing aircraft and electronics industries, for example, show among the highest ratios of research outlays to sales of all industry, while the relatively slow-growing primary-metal and food industries exhibit extremely low ratios.

The relative importance of various types of research naturally differs among industries. For example, the constant development of new and improved *products* is of vital necessity to the drug industry; the discovery of new *processes* is an important consideration for the petroleum industry; and finding a way to tap new *markets* is essential in the aluminum industry.

Research promotes interindustry competition, which is good both for the industries involved and for the nation. Inasmuch as industries contend for the same consumer dollars, the results of research may permit one industry to forge ahead of another. Research thus is both productive and vitally necessary for the health of any industry, and many a firm has passed from the business scene because of failure to perform realistic research. Among these are producers of water wheels, gas fixtures and lamps, oil cloth, and carriages.

A good example of the impact of technological change may be found in the case of Servel, Inc. This firm made buggies in the early 1900's, switched to gas refrigerators in the 1920's, and finally announced that it would sell its physical assets, go out of the appliance business, and acquire a new and different type of business. Obviously, the industries that will be leading the parade tomorrow are those that are research-minded today.

IMPORTANCE TO THE INDIVIDUAL FIRM

Although research, as practiced today, is still new enough to retain some of its pioneer characteristics, it has achieved general acceptance as a tool of valuable assistance in reaching overall company objectives. In most well-managed firms, the research organization is now considered to be in the same category with the sales force, the advertising staff, or the manufacturing function as a contributor to the success of the enterprise; and the research director qualifies as one of the regular members of the top management team.

Obviously, the importance attached to the activity implies the existence of specific corporate objectives of long-range goals and of a plan for reaching them. If these goals do not exist, the situation is comparable to that of a rudderless ship, adrift on a chartless sea, where blind expedience must substitute for alert intelligence. Such objectives are a prerequisite to the formulation of sound criteria for evaluating research.

PROBLEMS IN EVALUATING RESEARCH

The general uncertainty of the incidence of exploitable research findings presents both a challenge and an opportunity to business management generally and to research administrators in particular. This vagueness makes it difficult to measure the gains from past research, to determine the proper scope of current effort, to establish a cut-off point for projects that appear fruitless, and to anticipate future gains. It is small wonder that research administrators are sometimes unsuccessful in convincing management of the profitability of expanding the research effort.

THE SERENDIPITY FACTOR

The well-publicized characteristic of research—namely, that important discoveries may result from completely accidental events—has been designated by the fifty-dollar word "serendipity." What is often more important, however, is the fact that the accidental discovery may prove to be of little value unless someone recognizes its significance. Consider, for example, the number of instances that the penicillin spore was observed by various scientists before Dr. Alexander Fleming appreciated its significance.

There are, fortunately, two offsetting factors to this general vagueness by which research is surrounded. First, precise results of a good many other activities carried on by the average business firm are difficult to measure afterward or to predict beforehand. The areas of public relations and personnel relations can be cited as examples.

Second, exceptions to the rule of uncertainty are occurring more frequently in industry as experience is acquired, as a historical record is built, and—more specifically—as new techniques are developed through the use of large numbers of repetitive tests whose outcome is subject to the laws of probability. The routine testing of soil samples for new antibiotics is a good example.

THREE ALLOCATION PROBLEMS

Practical research administration seems to require three allocation decisions: (1) how much capital to devote to research; (2) how to distribute the research budget between types of research—that is, between basic or applied, product or process development; and (3) how to direct research activity into the most profitable specific avenues or projects. The remainder of this discussion is concerned with some guides that have proved helpful in making these decisions. Most of them are qualitative rather than quantitative, and many require the exercise of informed, subjective judgment.

TOTAL RESEARCH EXPENDITURE

Any intelligent approach to the question of how much of a firm's total financial resources should be devoted to research involves the answers to several basic questions.

First, assuming that one of the company's objectives is to attain or maintain industrial leadership, to what degree is research a necessary prerequisite? Obviously, some study of the practices of present leaders in the industry is necessary, for "you can't argue much with success." Regardless of the industry in which the firm is active, some amount of research is sure to pay off. As has been implied above, however, certain fields demand a greater research effort than others.

Another important question is how the present research effort compares in size with that of competitors. In examining this factor, it is insufficient to consider merely the total dollar expenditure. The aggregate should be compared to reveal differences that exist between the company and its competitors with respect to sales, product mix, objectives, and available resources. When allowances are made for such differences, the size of the research effort is seen in proper perspective.

A closely related question involves research in the past. Has it been as productive as that of comparable companies? This aspect should be evaluated in the light of the total amount spent. Obviously, the productivity of the activity will depend not only upon the efficiency with which the research is planned, conducted, and controlled but also upon the quality of the technology, personnel, and facilities available and upon the directions taken by the research effort. An appraisal of productivity might profitably include a review of the magnitude and the number of scientific articles published and of the number of patents obtained. Each of these factors should be related to the amount of the research expenditure and the number of scientists employed, and the trend in the ratio of expenditure to scientific personnel should be inspected. Of course, none of these quantitative determinations can be used as a final measure of productivity, but they can all serve as useful guides. The trends revealed are likely to be more significant than any absolute magnitudes.

SOME ALTERNATIVE COURSES

Still another point to be considered is whether to do one's own research, to purchase patents, or to enter into licensing agreements. There usually should not be a fixed policy in this regard. Each project should be considered on its own merits in relation to such factors as availability of patents, the competitive situation, relative costs, and resources available; the vested interest existing in products or processes previously developed is also important.

Inasmuch as the same ends can often be achieved through different means, it is worthwhile to compare the increases in output (in specific areas) that have been secured through research in the past with increases in output achieved through expansion of plant and facilities. Such investigation should relate to both results and costs. Since capital is never available in unlimited amounts, one should attempt to compare the rate of return on an investment in plant and equipment with that likely to be secured if a similar amount is invested in research.

Finally, somewhere along the line, it should be determined whether the firm's objectives are being met currently—and, if not, whether the research program is at fault. This calls, of course, for a broad re-examination of the firm's objectives and of the contribution made by research toward reaching them in the past.

Carefully weighed answers to these questions will, in most cases, at least set limits on the research expenditure feasible for a firm.

FORMULA APPROACHES

We are convinced that to search for a formula or rule of thumb with which to determine how much capital to devote to research is to pursue a will-o'-the-wisp. Too many intangible factors are involved for this difficult question to be reduced to a formula. Moreover, the algebra or arithmetic involved in a given formula will never render a result any more perfect or reliable than the individual ingredients that go into the equation. The absolute amounts derived by application of a formula are seldom significant. In some cases, however, comparison of such results derived for a firm with those derived for a competitor may have meaning; at other times, the change in results over a period of time may be of interest.

Keeping the limitations and qualifications applying to the use of this approach in mind, it is interesting to consider some of the formulas which have been used by various companies in the past. These include:

- Comparison of research expenditure with sales gain over a period.
- Comparison of research expenditure with the ratio of sales of new products to sales of all products.
- Comparison of research expenditure with change in market share over a certain period.
- Determination of research expenditure per employee.
- Comparison of rate of net profit (anticipated or actually derived) from investment in research with the current rates of return on plant, property, and equipment, or on invested capital. (In this connection, allowance should be made for any differences in the timing of receipts, for the return is apt to be deferred longer for research expenditures than for investment in plant, property, and equipment.)
- Multiplication of the expected rate of return from the research expenditure by a measure of the probability of deriving such a return (a variation of the preceding formula).
- Comparison of the amount of research expenditure with the amount of selling, advertising, or manufacturing expense.

A McGraw-Hill study has suggested that there is an average lag of at least seven years from the beginning of research on a new product until the product is ready for large-scale output—perhaps five years for research and two for developing markets—and that plant expenditures may lag another two years. Time lags probably do average out to something approaching these periods; but, owing to the irregularity of occurrence of important research discoveries, it is virtually impossible to measure the lag for any individual firm. As a matter of fact, specific case characteristics distort the results of most such formulas.

One further word of caution: in any formulas using research expenditures, the amounts should be adjusted to account for the rising costs of research as well as for the growing complexity of research as the frontiers of accomplishment are pushed forward.

After considering these formulas from the standpoint of logic and of their application to particular cases, it is obvious that all should be viewed with a certain degree of skepticism and that none should be relied upon to the exclusion of qualitative considerations.

DISTRIBUTION BY TYPE

Determination of the total amount to be spent on research is generally made by persons in the higher echelons of management, after considering the recommendations of the research administrator. However, distribution of the research budget between research types—basic or applied, product or process development—presents many problems and is generally left to the research administrator.

The problem of definition of terms is sometimes important here, particularly in comparing the distribution of funds in one company with that in another. Basic research may be defined as activity directed toward the improvement of fundamental knowledge without the objective of developing specific new products or processes or of making improvements in existing ones. Thus, research into the cause of the common cold would be considered basic research, while investigation of possible cures for the common cold would be considered applied research.

INDUSTRY'S RESPONSIBILITY TO CARRY ON RESEARCH

In determining the distribution of the research budget between the two types of research, some consideration ought to be given to industry's responsibility to engage in basic research. This question breaks down into two parts: what obligation does industry have to *finance* basic research in our economy, and what responsibility does it have to *perform* the basic research?

To take a very broad view of the matter, answers to these questions depend largely upon where one stands on the controversial issue of private versus public enterprise—and therefore involve considerations of relative efficiency, costs, profitability, and the facilities and technology available. For a business firm, however, a narrower viewpoint is generally taken, since responsibility for either financing or performing basic research is interrelated with the firm's obligations to its owners.

Thus, the questions boil down to determining the amount of profit likely to result from the products, processes, or improvements that might be developed as a result of the basic research. Because profit prospects are ordinarily vague at this stage, the matter is frequently resolved in favor of financing basic research elsewhere than in industry and of performing the work wherever the greatest efficiency can be attained. The alternatives to industrial support of research are, of course, the university, private nonprofit foundations, and Government agencies, each of which has its advantages and disadvantages.

THE INDIVIDUAL FIRM'S CAPACITY TO PERFORM RESEARCH

Other areas which should be explored in determining the distribution of the research budget are the firm's needs and objectives—and, in view thereof, the firm's strengths and weaknesses. It is also necessary to consider what technology, equipment, and personnel are available to perform the work. Furthermore, it is important to review past accomplishments to learn the relative profitability of basic research as compared with applied research.

Another consideration sometimes overlooked is the company's ability to utilize the results in each area. Does the company have available the organization, management ability, facilities, and funds necessary to follow the steps required to derive a profit from the basic or applied research?

QUALITATIVE CONSIDERATIONS

In allocating funds to basic and applied research, several other factors ought to be investigated. One of these is the effect of the distribution of research expenditure on the performance of other firms in the particular industry and other industries. Quantitative data bearing on this question are rather limited, but any deficiencies in research results should be considered to determine whether they arise primarily because of the division of the funds or because of the manner in which such funds are administered. Where possible, it is worthwhile to determine what savings in the cost of manufacture or distribution have been achieved in the past through process research and what the cost of research has been as compared with returns derived from the new products developed.

As is the case in determining the total amount to be spent on research, this matter of allocating research funds to the two types of activity is best approached in qualitative terms with the exercise of informed judgment. This approach emphasizes the importance of giving the research administrator considerable freedom in making such allocations.

CHOOSING SPECIFIC PROJECTS

The next step in planning the details of the research activity is that of channeling the research into the most profitable individual projects. Instead of looking for a market to suit a particular product which has resulted from research, it is generally more profitable to look ahead to the fast-growing markets of the future through the use of suitable statistical techniques, economic analyses, market research, and informed imagination, and to direct the company's research toward these growing markets and toward the objectives and goals of the firm's long-range plans.

THE CHECKLIST APPROACH

Each proposal should be subjected to rigid tests to determine three important facts: (1) its technical feasibility from an engineering and manufacturing viewpoint; (2) its marketability (if a new product) from the aspect of distribution methods required and of consumer tastes; and (3) its potential profitability in the light of the projected sales volume, price, cost of production, and availability and cost of capital. On the pages following (232 and 233) is a checklist with some 50 qualitative factors to consider in evaluating a research project.

A similar type of list, suggested by one authority, Theodore T. Miller, is designed to be employed in an interesting manner.[1] The proposal under consideration is rated *very good, good, average, poor,* or *very poor* with respect to each factor listed, and the ratings for each grade are totaled and compared with corresponding totals for other proposed projects. In my opinion, the greatest value of this checklist approach lies in the requirement for reviewing the project from the standpoint of each of the factors rather than in any final "score."

OLIN'S "INDEX OF RETURN" FORMULA

Another technique sometimes used in evaluating individual projects was devised a number of years ago by Fred Olsen of Olin Mathieson Chemical Corporation. This approach involves the calculation of an "index of return" formula. The first term of the numerator is determined as follows: for a process improvement, the full value of savings for one year; for a product improvement, 2 per cent of sales of the product for two years; and for a new product, 3 per cent of sales of the product for five years. Both the time periods and the percentages used have varied over the years. The research project should be abandoned if the value of the index falls below 3.

$$\text{Index of return} = \frac{\begin{array}{c}\text{Estimated value}\\\text{of research}\\\text{if it succeeds}\end{array} \times \begin{array}{c}\text{Estimated}\\\text{chance of}\\\text{success}\end{array}}{\text{Estimated cost of research}}$$

[1] Miller, Theodore T., "Projecting the Profitability of New Products," *The Commercialization of Research Results,* Special Report 20, American Management Association, New York, 1957.

Source of Information

Factor	Accounting	Budget	Economist	Engineering	Manufacturing	Market Research	New-Product Development	Research	Sales	Traffic	Treasurer
Research proper											
Technology								✓			
Personnel								✓			
Facilities								✓			
Type of research								✓			
Production											
Technical feasibility				✓				✓			
Requirements to meet competition											
a. Production time				✓							
b. Physical properties								✓			
c. Skills required				✓							
d. Special materials								✓			
Customers' specifications											
Physical properties						✓		✓			
Sizes, colors, etc.						✓					
Potential demand											
Magnitude, current and prospective			✓			✓					
Customers					✓				✓		
Market share					✓		✓		✓		
Distribution methods									✓		
Scale of plant											
Technical factors				✓	✓						
Special demand characteristics			✓	✓	✓	✓					
Location of plant											
Raw materials								✓			
Labor								✓			
Customers						✓					
Nature of customers						✓					
Transportation costs										✓	
Operations											
Sales projections			✓			✓			✓		
Cost estimates				✓	✓						
Pro forma statements	✓	✓							✓		
Competition											
Prices, costs, and profits						✓					
Competitive advantages						✓			✓		

Source of Information

Factor	Accounting	Budget	Economist	Engineering	Manufacturing	Market Research	New-Product Development	Research	Sales	Traffic	Treasurer
Pricing to achieve objectives											
Profit	√	√					√				
Market share						√	√		√		
Volume							√		√		
Capital requirements and profits											
Return on research outlay	√	√									
Return on other new investment required	√	√									
Investment alternatives			√			√	√				
Relation to long-term plan											
Use of facilities in common					√				√		
Unique features of new product											
a. Special sales training									√		
b. Handling and shipping					√						
c. Spoilage					√				√		
Process research: Effect of process change											
Time					√			√			
Material or labor					√			√			
Safety					√			√			
Quality								√	√		
Appearance								√	√		
Measuring gains											
Pro forma statements	√								√		
Return on research outlay	√	√									
Return on other investment required	√	√									
Financing capital requirements											
Long-term capital budget											
a. Cash flow			√								√
b. Payout period		√									√
c. Return on investment		√									√
Availability of new capital											√
Cost of new capital											√
Risk											
Product life						√					
Relation to general business fluctuations						√					
Strategic importance of product						√					

Obviously, there is nothing really unique about this formula. It merely sets down in mathematical style a method for determining what amounts to a rate of return on investment in plant or equipment. We are not aware that there is any particular logical or quantitative support for the suggested alternative values for the first term of the numerator. The percentages appear to be more or less arbitrary, which means that the absolute magnitude of the index of return is not particularly significant. However, comparisons of the index for various alternative research projects may be of value.

MILLER'S VARIATION

A variation of this formula, apparently applicable only to new products, was suggested by Theodore Miller. His formula merely spells out in somewhat more detail the steps necessary to derive the return on the research expenditure. In the numerator of this formula, the following factors are multiplied: (1) percentage chance of technical success, (2) percentage chance of commercial success, (3) estimated unit sale per year, (4) profit per unit, and (5) the square root of the life of the product stated in years. The total cost of the research project is the denominator. The indicated division yields a "product number," which provides a basis for comparison of various research proposals.

The changes in the Olsen formula suggested by Mr. Miller seem to be sound in both logic and arithmetic, with perhaps one exception. There is no apparent logical reason for using the square root of the life of the product rather than the life itself, even though it does make the result more conservative. At the same time, moreover, it renders the result incomparable with rates of return derived by customary methods in connection with investment in plant and equipment.

Mr. Miller's formula would be further improved if, instead of using the square root of the product's life, he modified the term so as to discount at a reasonable rate of interest the future return on the research investment.[2] The formula thus modified is not really further complicated, for the value of the term suggested as a substitution for the "square root of life" term can be determined readily from a table showing the present worth of an annuity.[3]

---

[2] The formula then would appear as $\frac{1-(1+i)n^{-n}}{i}$, where i is annual rate of interest and n is number of years of life.

[3] The difference between Mr. Miller's original formula and my modifications may be illustrated in the case of a product having a life of nine years and calling for a discount rate of 3 per cent. In the original formula, the value of the term "square root of life" would obviously be 3, while in the modified form (as shown in a present-worth table), the value of the term would be 7.79.

* * *

Any investigation of a given research proposal should be coordinated to include such specialized company functions as research, engineering, sales, market research, manufacturing, finance, and staff economists. In other words, this should be a team effort. However, it is important to leave the ultimate decision in the hands of the research administrator, since he has the responsibility for carrying out the work.

The criteria for evaluating research which have been discussed in this paper could be summarized in one word—*profitability*—for this must always be the overriding consideration. Whether the analysis be quantitative or qualitative, it should be oriented in this direction. Furthermore, profitability ought not to be considered in a vacuum. Whether the question deals with the total amount to be spent on research, with the allocation of research funds between types of research, or with a particular research proposal, estimated profitability should be compared with the potential profitability of any possible alternative action.

Finally, success in any research effort requires a company management that will assume responsibility, maintain objectivity, and take calculated risks on the basis of informed judgment. Above all, the executives must be alert, imaginative, and "sold" on research.

INDEX